Ready Steady Maths

First Class Pupil's Book

Betty Stoutt
Mary Ryan

Carroll Heinemann

Contents

How many?

Count and colour.

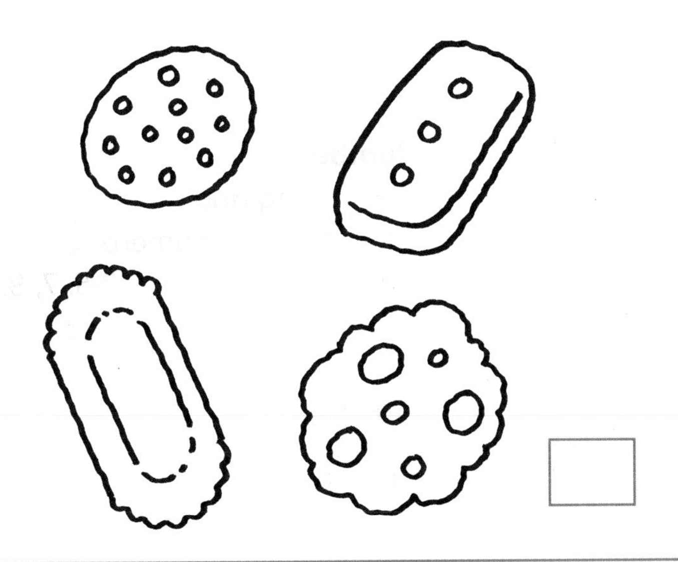

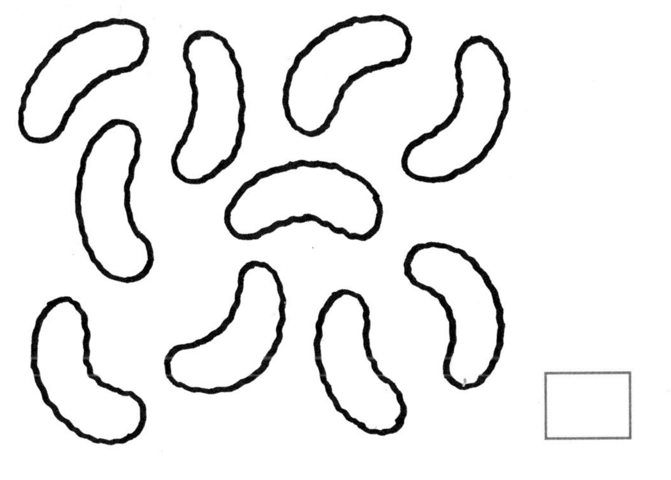

How many?

How many?

Draw one more spot. How many now?

Addition

Add

$2 + 1 = \square$

$3 + 3 = \square$

$5 + 1 = \square$

$2 + 2 = \square$

$4 + 4 = \square$

$4 + 3 = \square$

Draw and write.

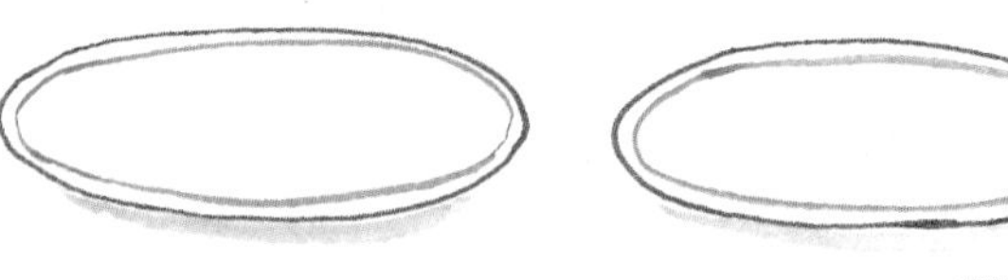

$5 + 2 = \square$

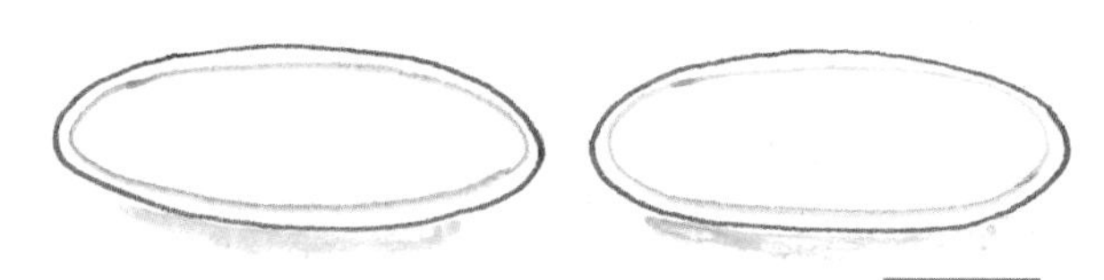

$4 + 1 = \square$

Who has the most cakes? ____________

Who has the least cakes? ____________

Zero

Add

3 + 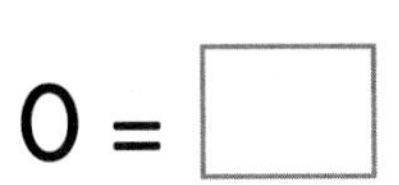 0 = ☐

0 + 4 = ☐

9 + 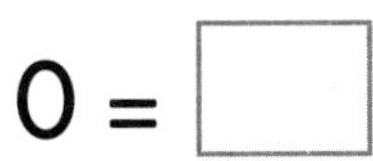 0 = ☐

0 + 2 = ☐

6 + 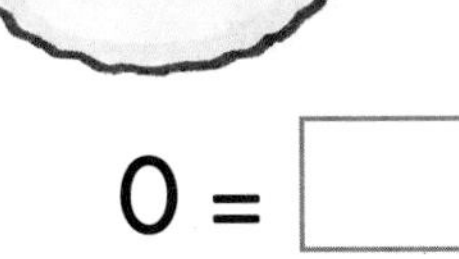 0 = ☐

0 + 8 = ☐

Draw and write.

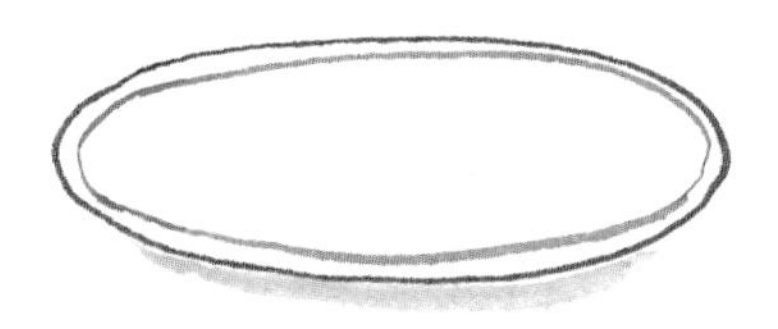 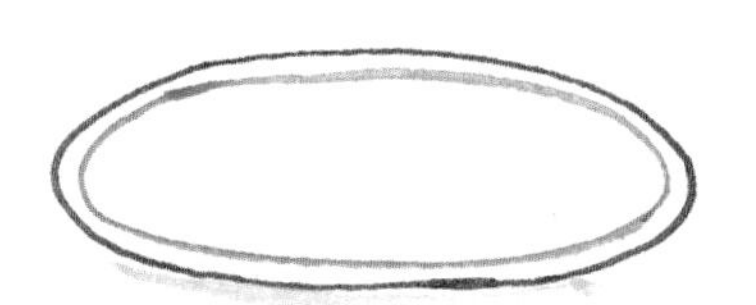

7 + 0 = ☐

Think
Talk
Niamh
Liam
Kim
Kate
Dan
Tom

Adding both ways

Add

3 + 2 = ☐

2 + 3 = ☐

5 + 1 = ☐

1 + 5 = ☐

4 + 3 = ☐

3 + 4 = ☐

Now try these.

4 + 2 = ☐

2 + 4 = ☐

7 + 2 = ☐

2 + 7 = ☐

5 + 3 = ☐

3 + 5 = ☐

6 + 4 = ☐

4 + 6 = ☐

4 + 1 = ☐

1 + 4 = ☐

5 + 4 = ☐

4 + 5 = ☐

Ten frame

Count

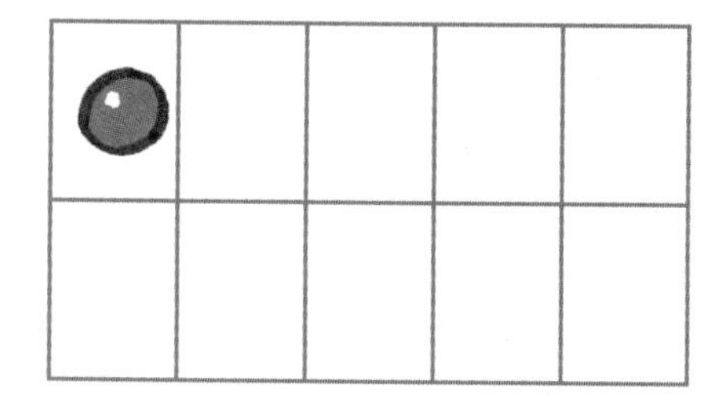

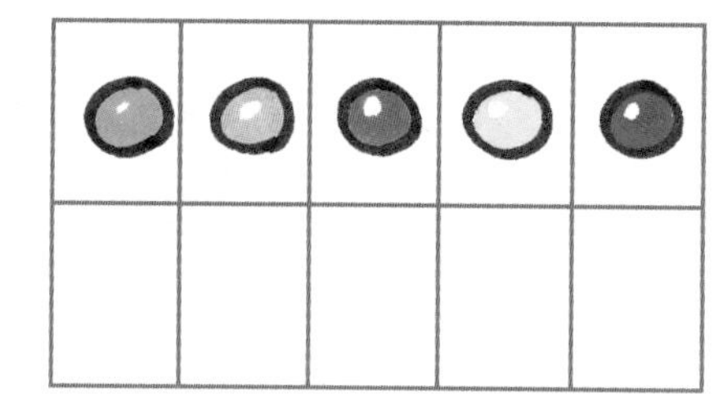

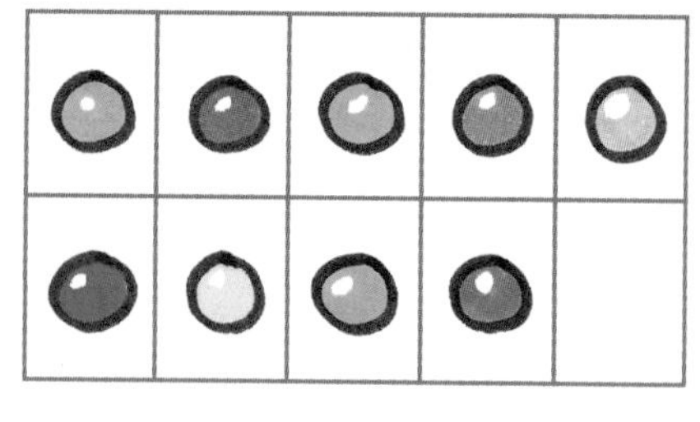

Show

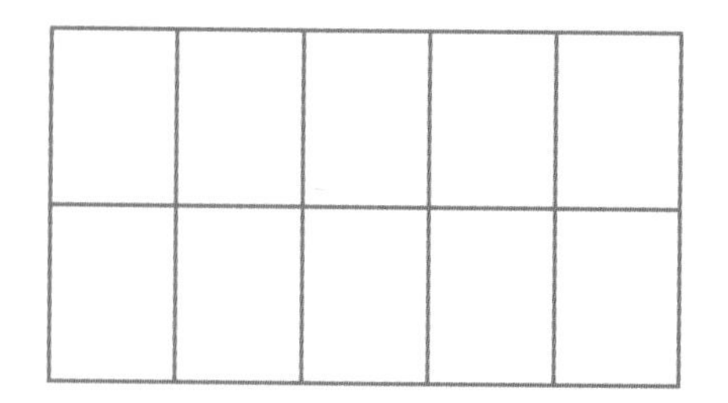

2

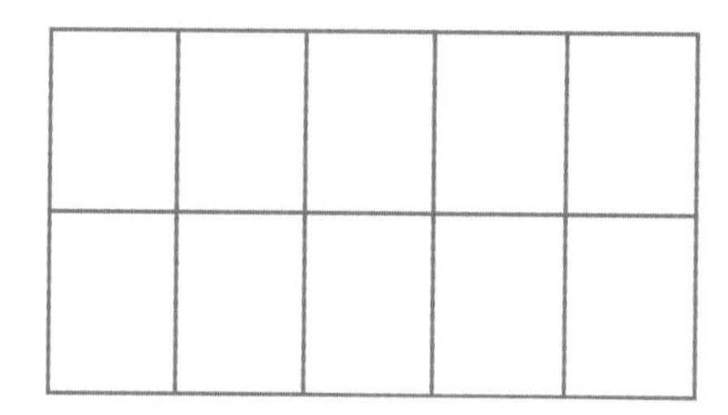

4

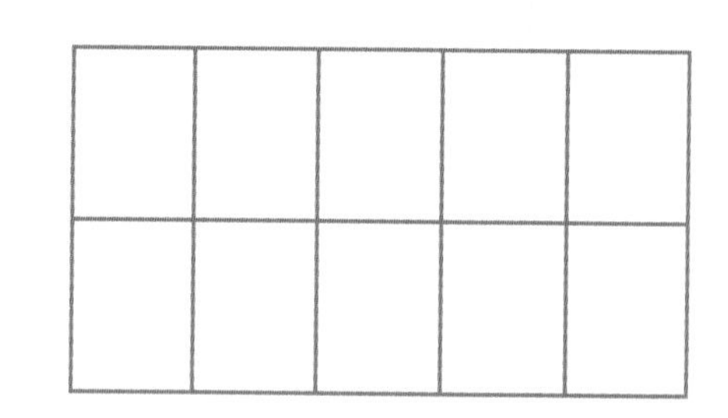

6

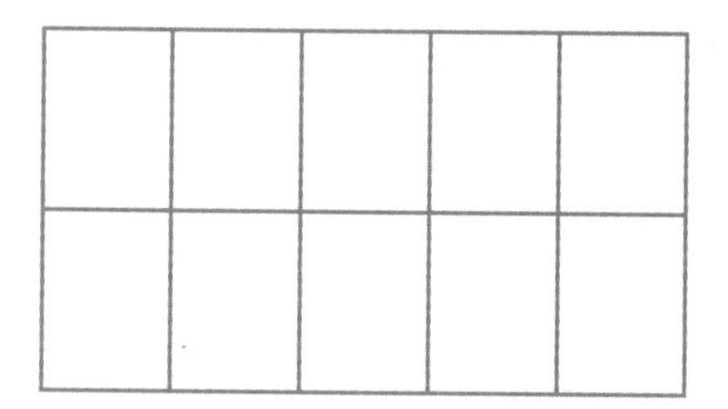

3

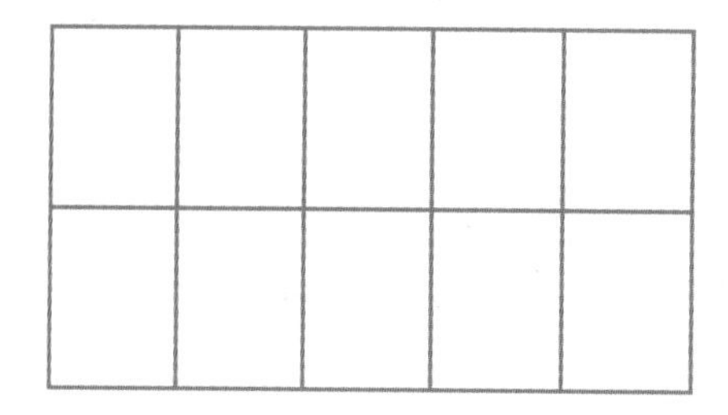

8

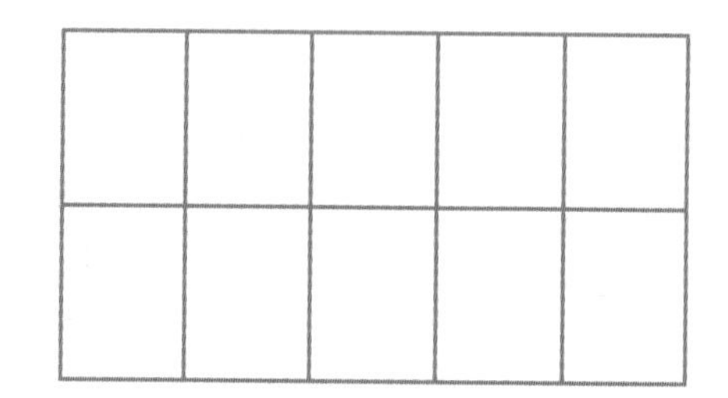

10

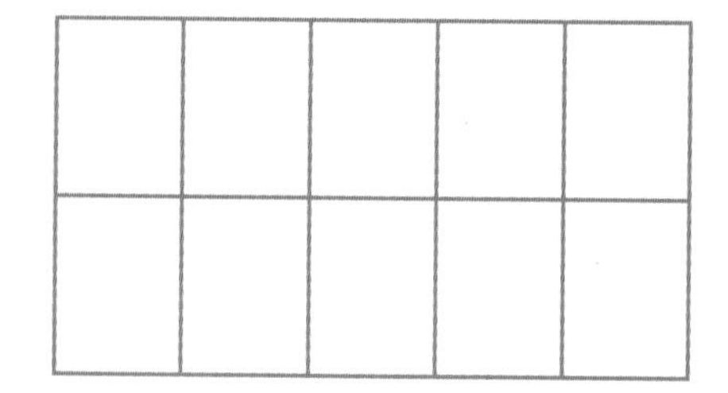

7

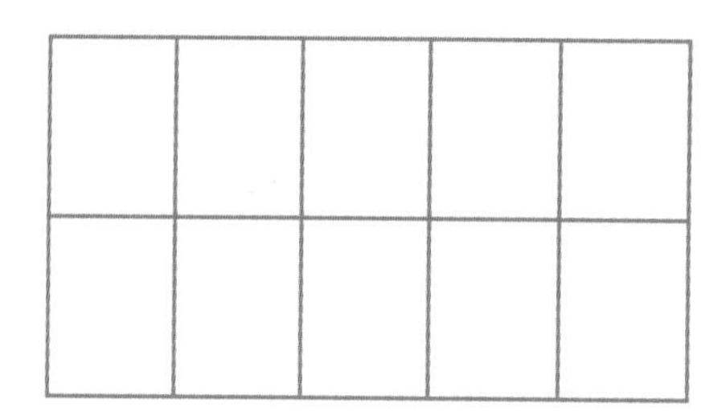

9

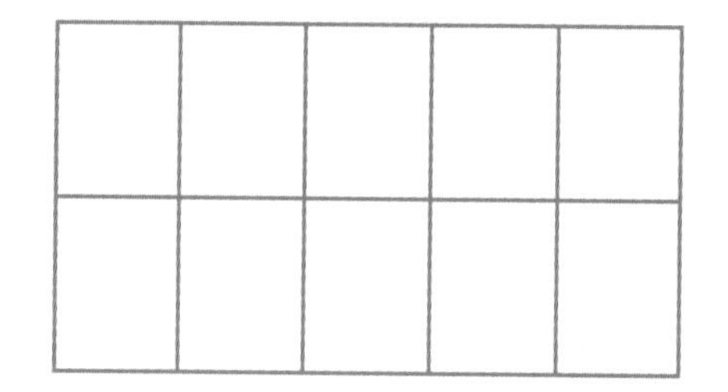

5

Making ten

Make 10

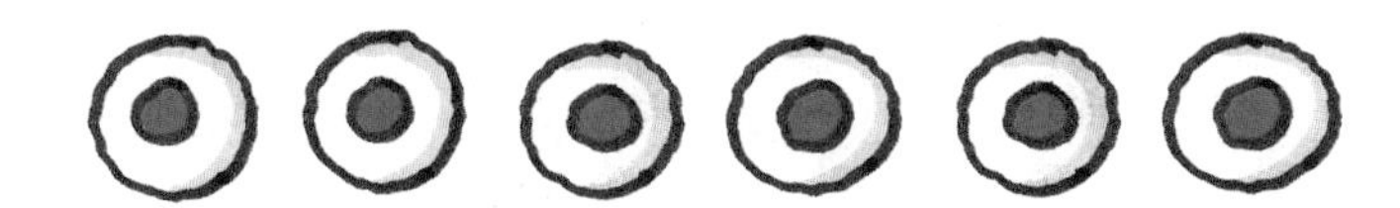

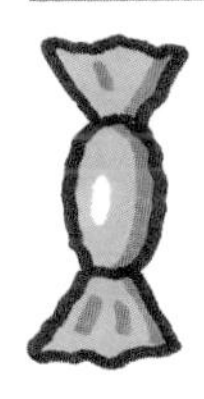

Draw candles and write.

six, seven, eight, nine, ten

Pattern

Extend the pattern.

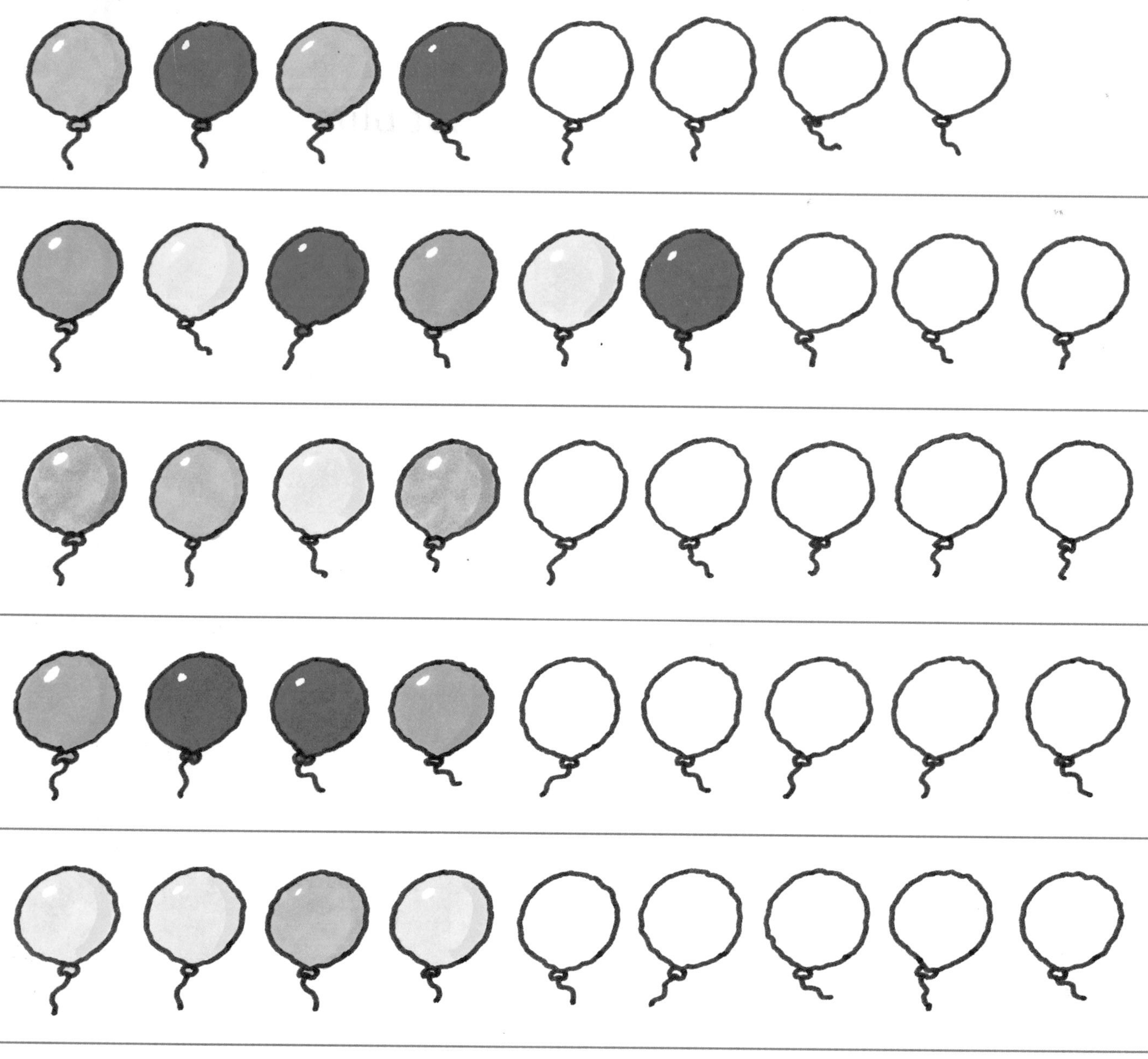

Make your own pattern.

Data

Kim wants to put only blue balloons on the table.
Help Kim to sort the balloons.

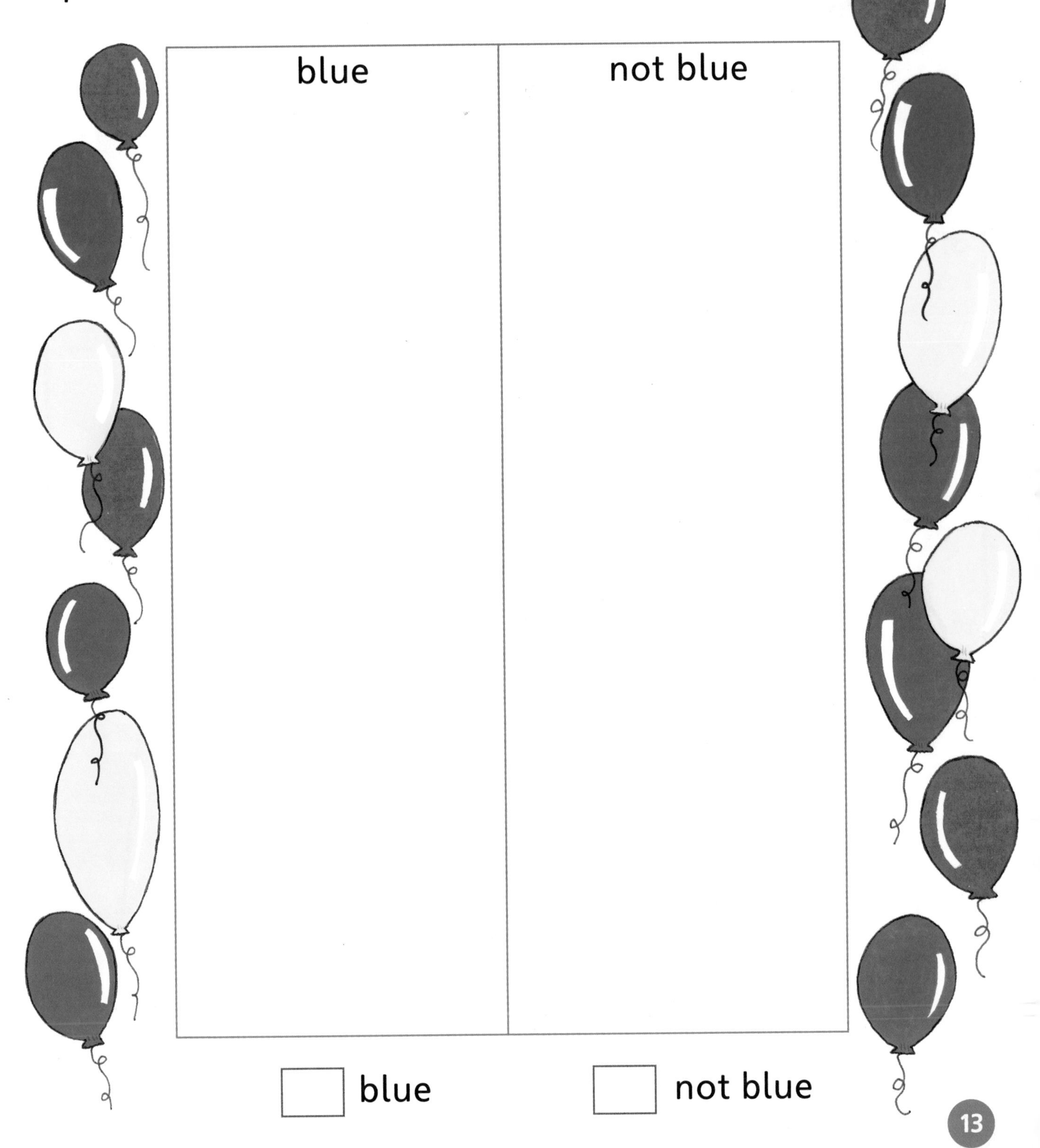

blue	not blue

☐ blue ☐ not blue

Shape

Colour

Subtraction –

How many?

children in all

go home

stay

children in all

go home

stay

children in all

go home

stay

children in all

go home

stay

children in all

go home

stay

Subtraction –

How many balloons are left?

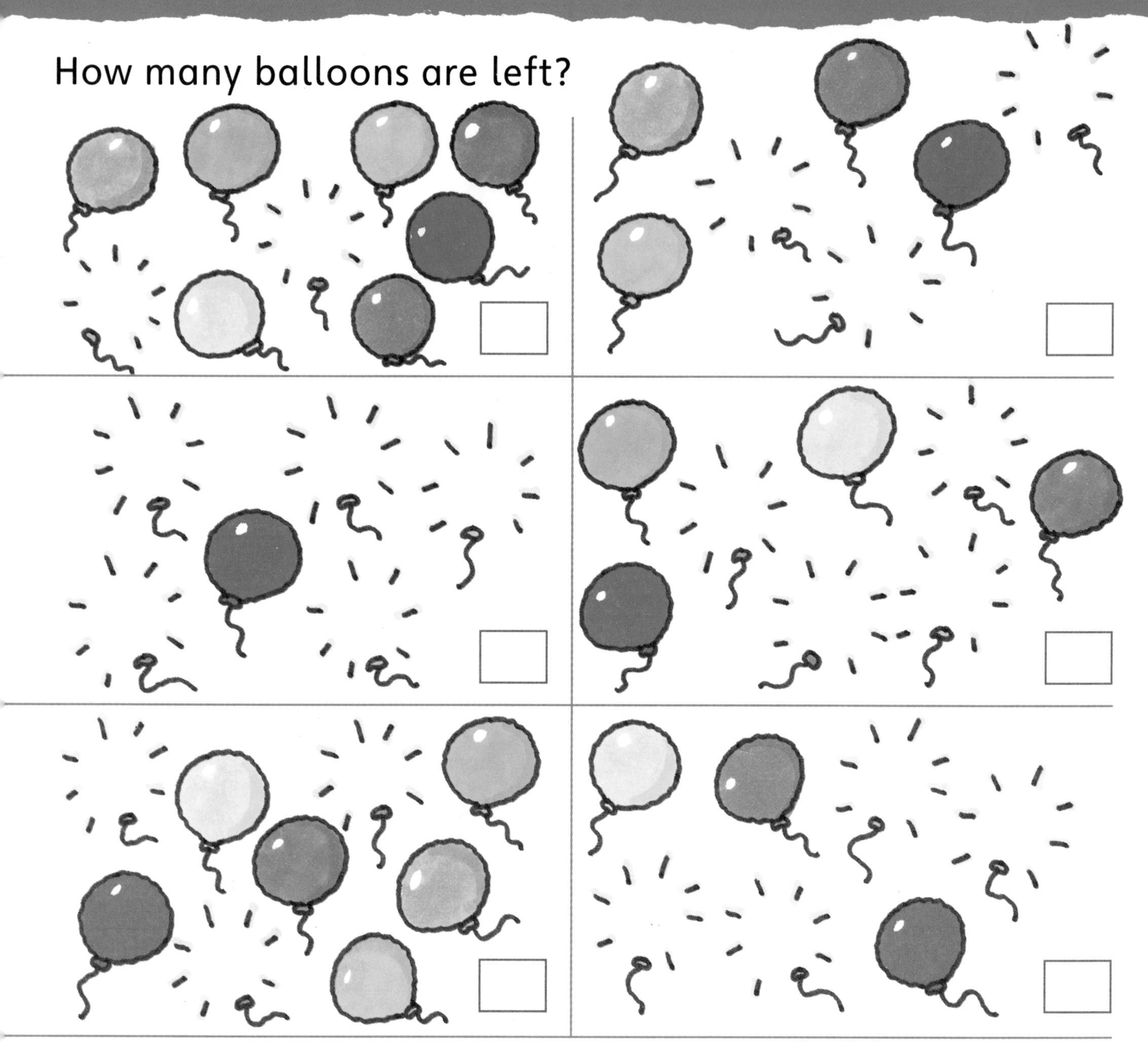

Draw and tell the story.

Subtraction –

How many cakes are left?

3 take away 1 = ☐

3 – 1 = ☐

4 take away 2 = ☐

4 – 2 = ☐

6 take away 1 = ☐

6 – 1 = ☐

5 take away 3 = ☐

5 – 3 = ☐

7 take away 2 = ☐

7 – 2 = ☐

8 take away 1 = ☐

8 – 1 = ☐

Subtraction –

How many cubes are left?

		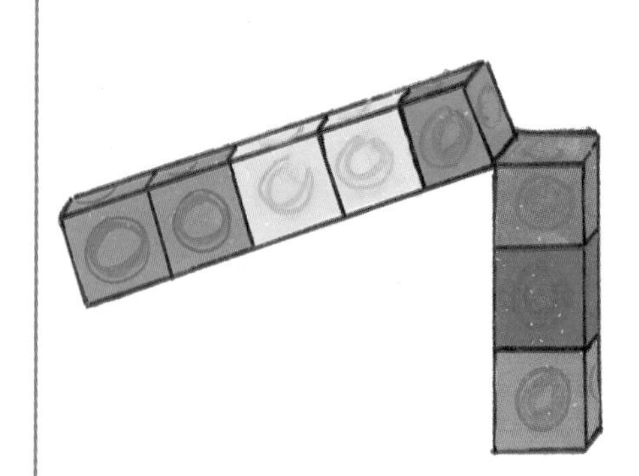
5 – 1 = ☐	6 – 2 = ☐	8 – 5 = ☐
		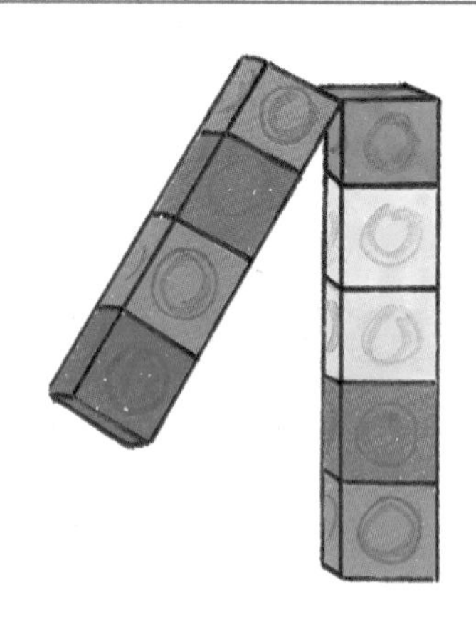
10 – 6 = ☐	7 – 2 = ☐	9 – 4 = ☐

Now try these. Use cubes.

6 – 3 = ☐	8 – 3 = ☐	10 – 5 = ☐	9 – 2 = ☐
10 – 4 = ☐	6 – 4 = ☐	8 – 6 = ☐	9 – 5 = ☐
7 – 5 = ☐	10 – 3 = ☐	6 – 5 = ☐	10 – 7 = ☐

Subtraction –

How many biscuits are left?

$3 - 3 =$ ☐

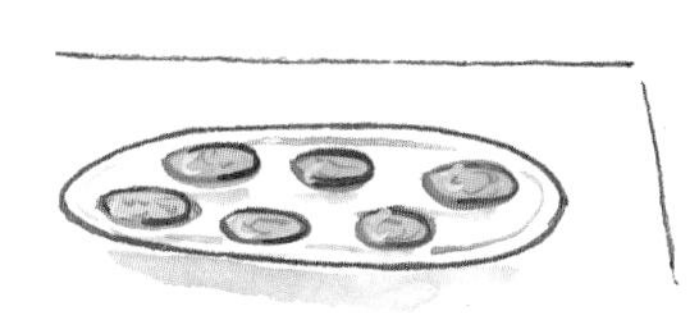

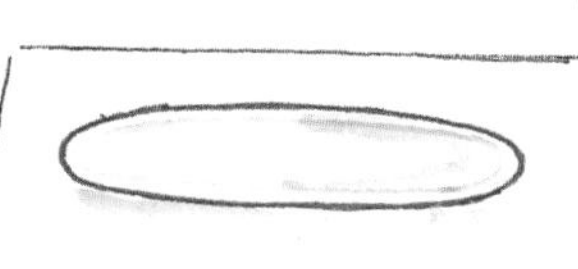

$6 - 6 =$ ☐

$2 - 2 =$ ☐

$5 - 5 =$ ☐

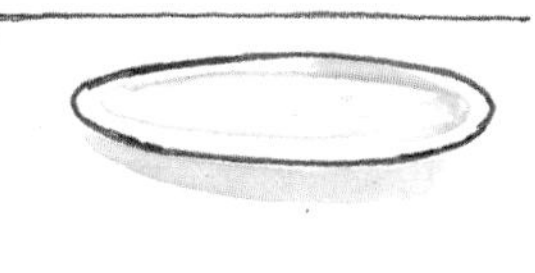

$4 - 4 =$ ☐

Missing numbers

Fill in the missing numbers.

1	2	3	4	5	6	7	8	9	10

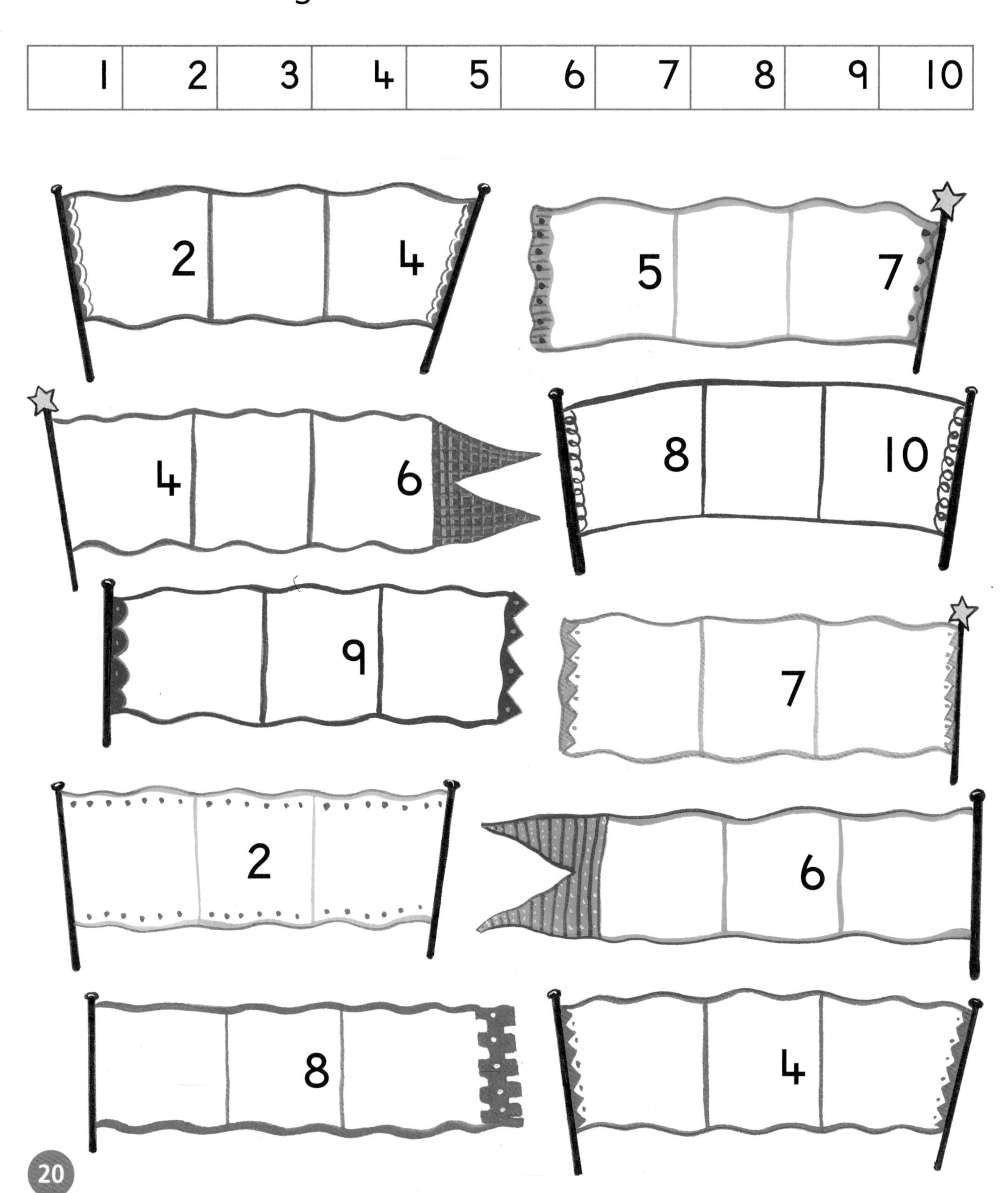

left right between

Draw

left right

left right

left right

left right

between

between

Days of the week

Write

Grouping in tens

How many bundles of ten candles are there?

How many candles are left over?

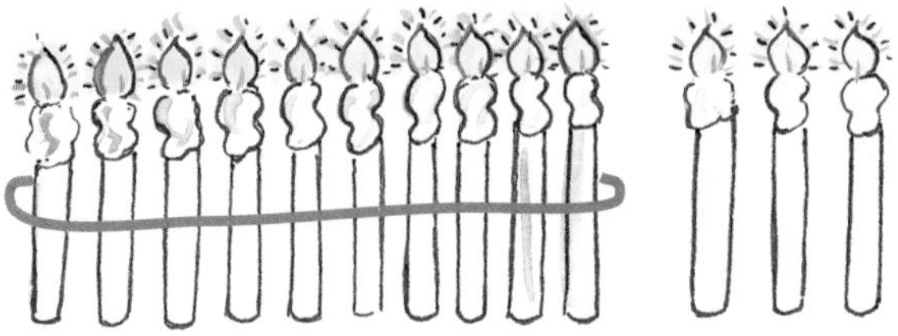

☐ ten

☐ units

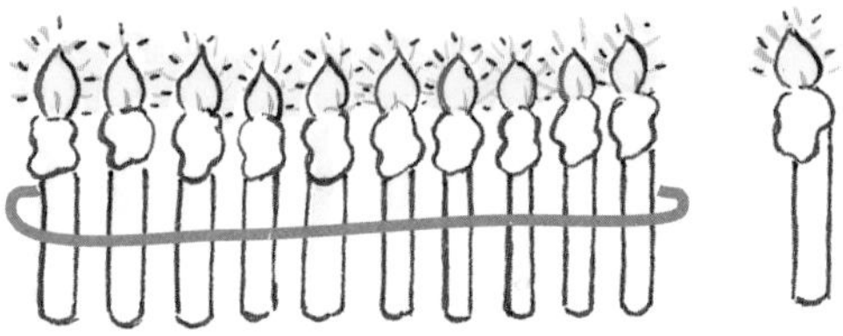

☐ ten

☐ units

☐ ten

☐ units

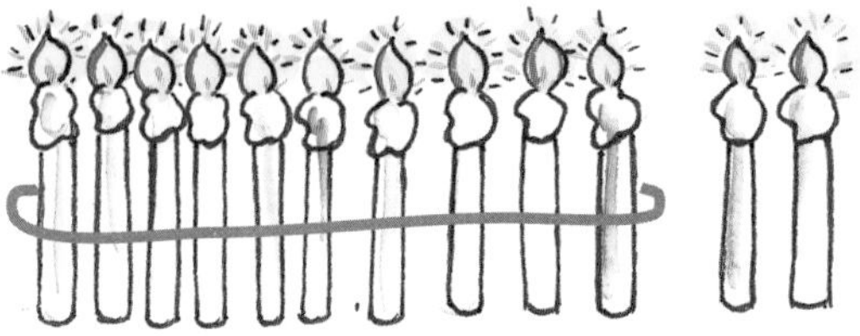

☐ ten

☐ units

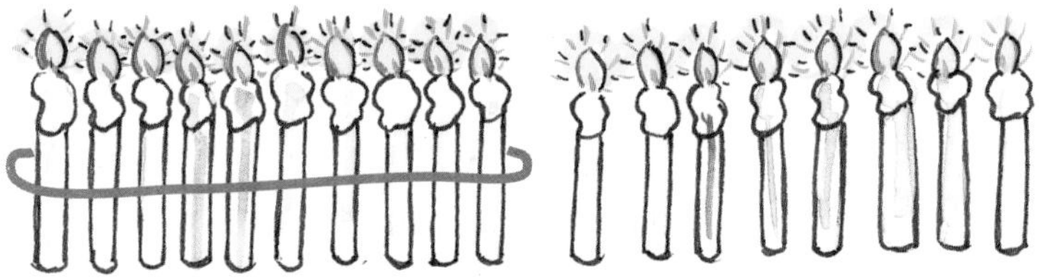

☐ ten

☐ units

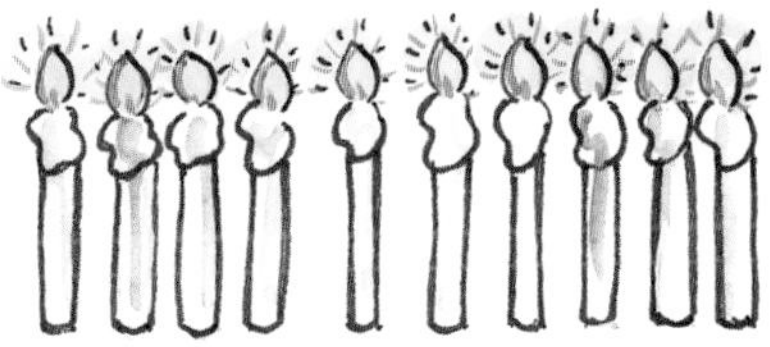

☐ ten

☐ units

Grouping in tens

The shopkeeper sells sweets in bags of ten. Ring the tens.
How many bags of ten sweets are there?
How many sweets are left over?

☐ ten
☐ units

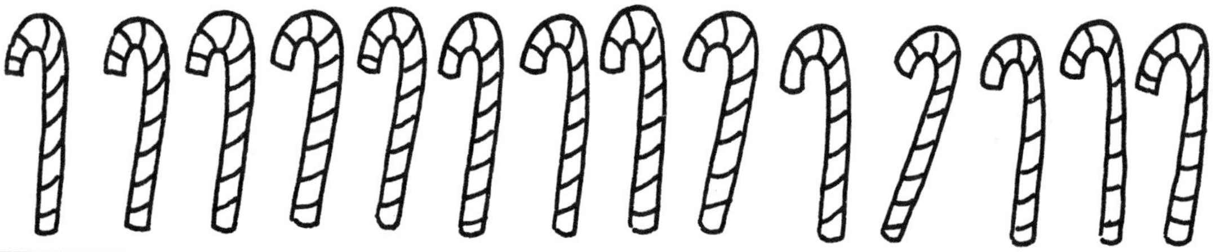

☐ ten
☐ units

☐ ten
☐ units

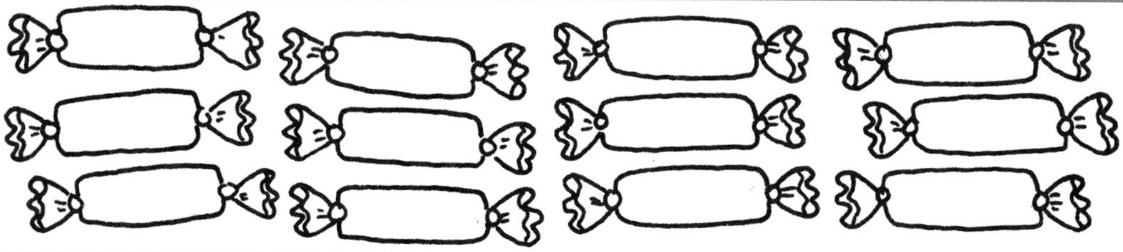

☐ ten
☐ units

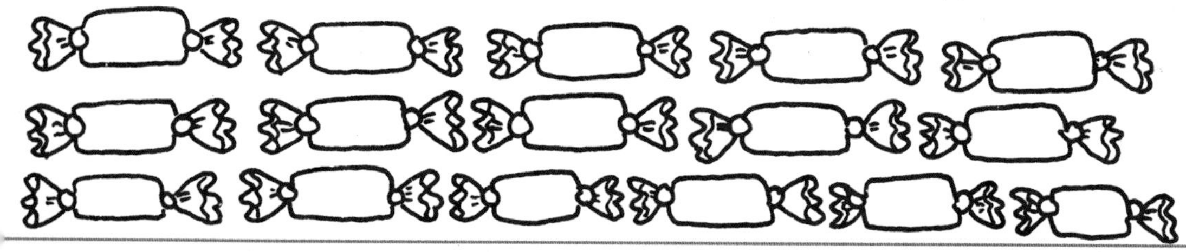

☐ ten
☐ units

☐ ten
☐ units

Grouping in tens

Ring the tens.

How many tens are there? How many straws are left?

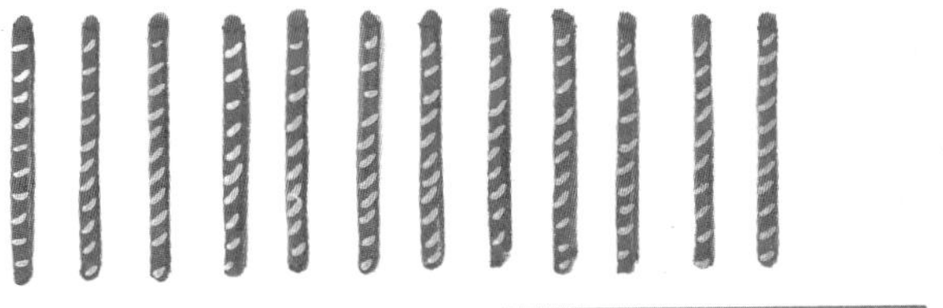

tens	units

tens	units

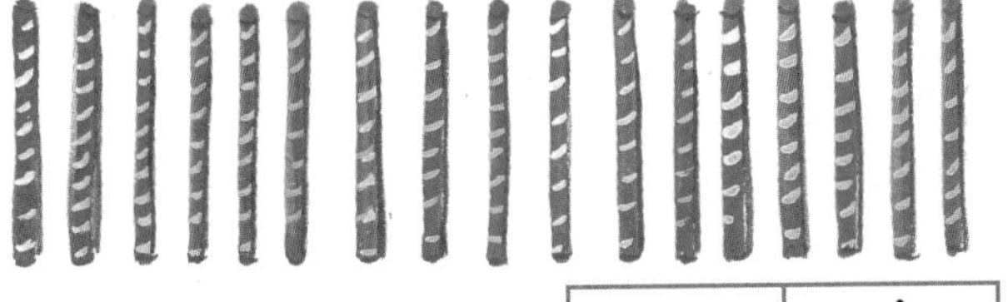

tens	units

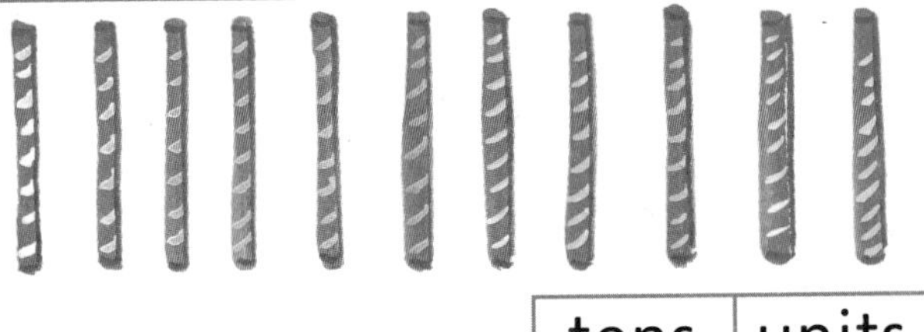

tens	units

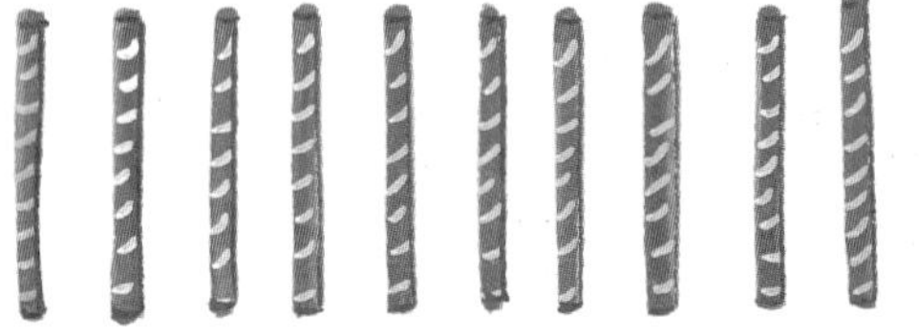

tens	units

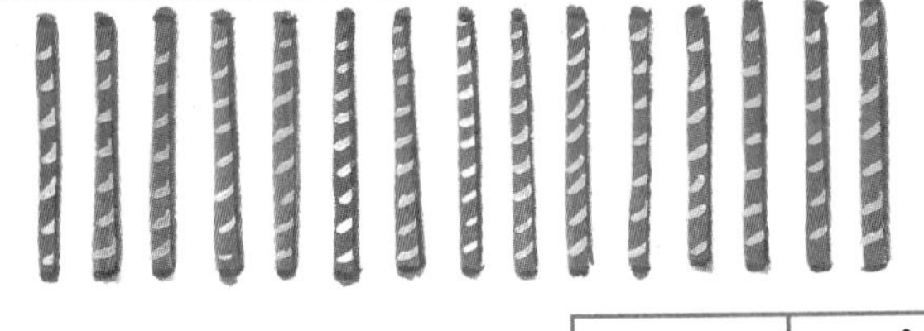

tens	units

tens	units

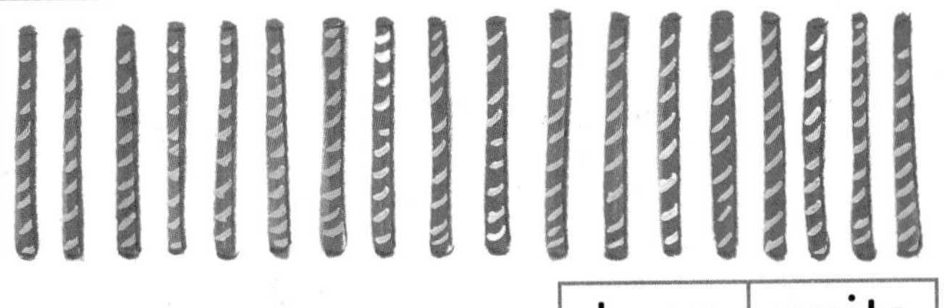

tens	units

Grouping in tens

How many?

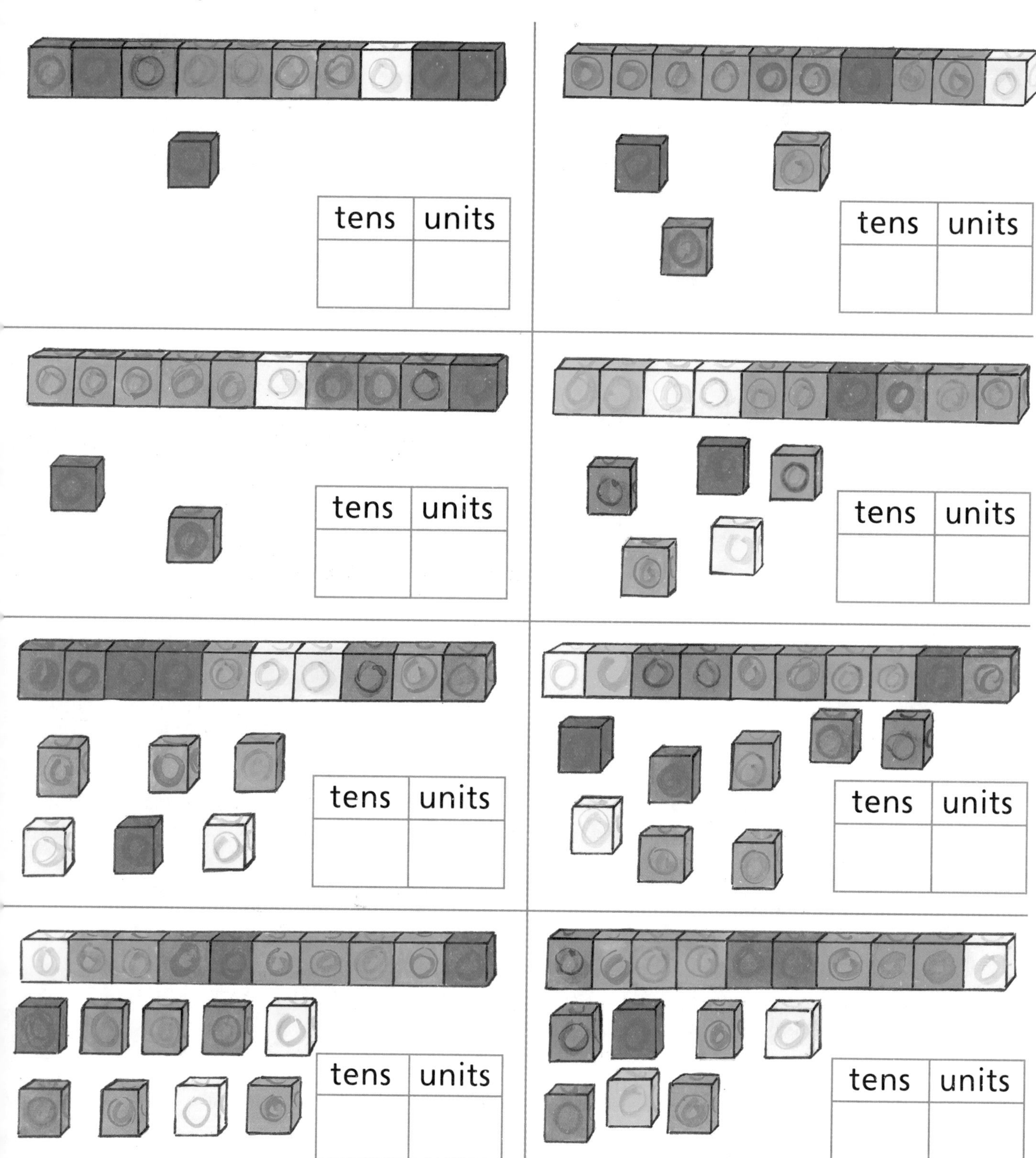

Think
Talk

Estimation

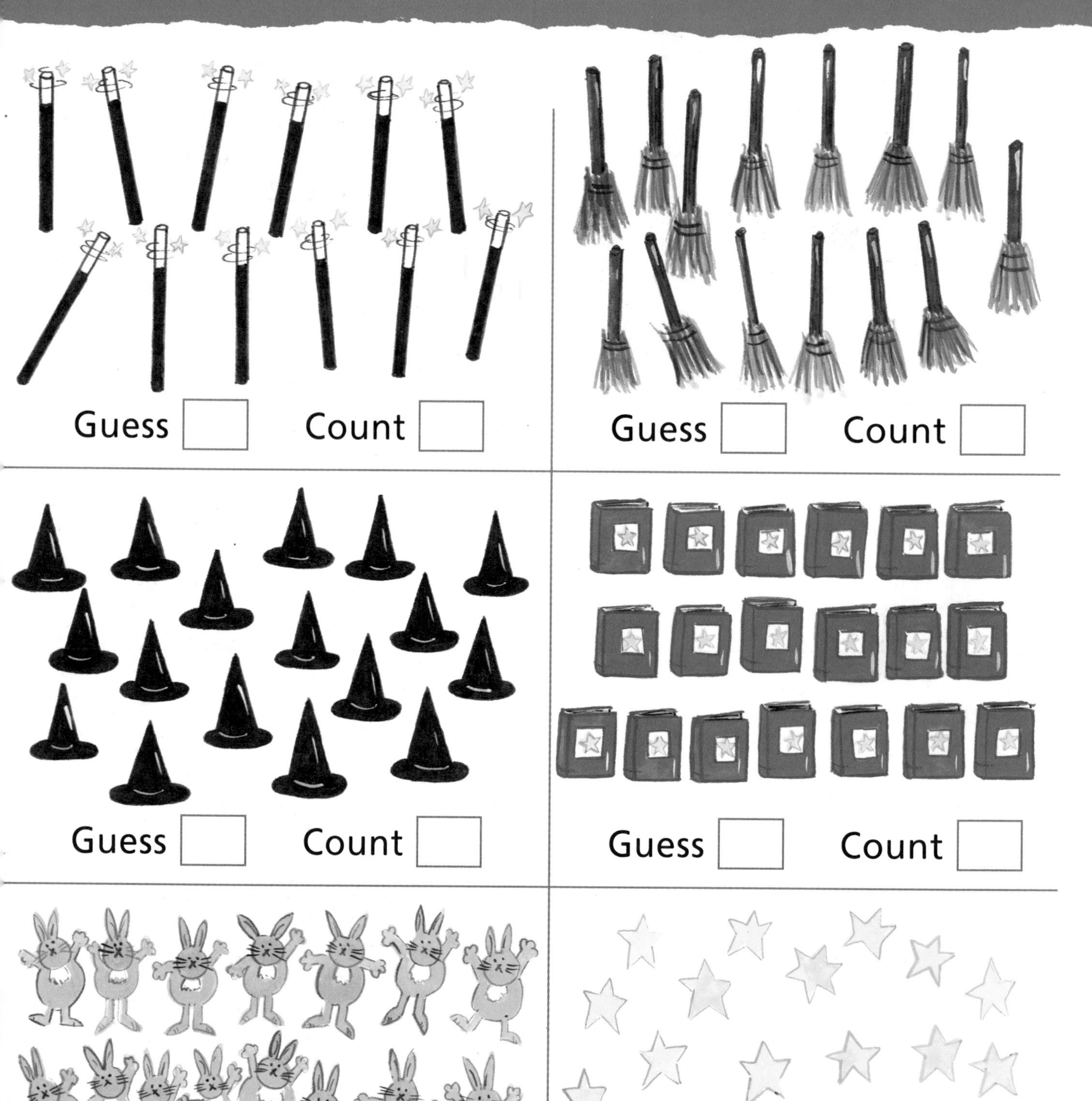

Guess Count

Guess Count

Guess Count

Guess Count

Guess Count

Guess Count

Count

Colour

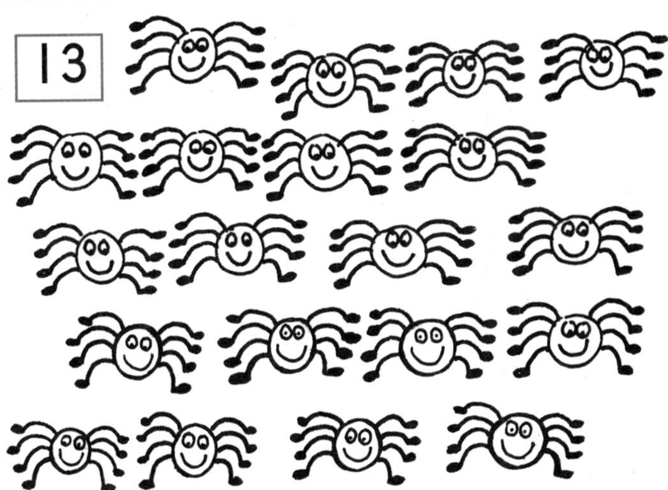

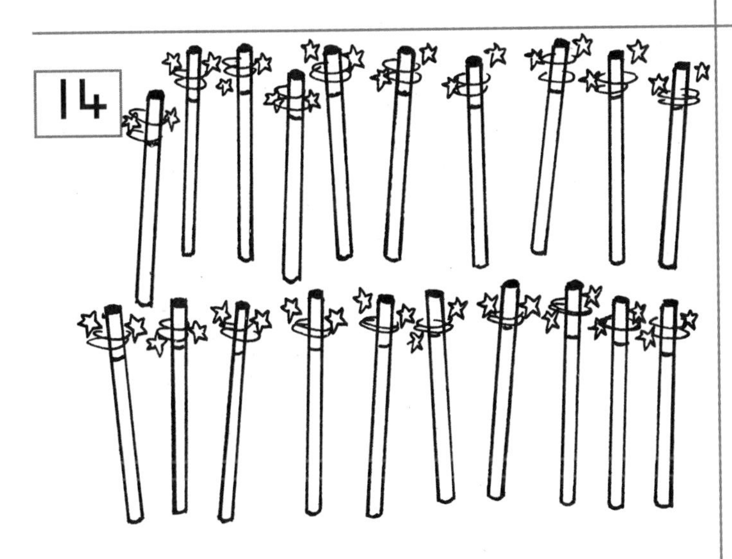

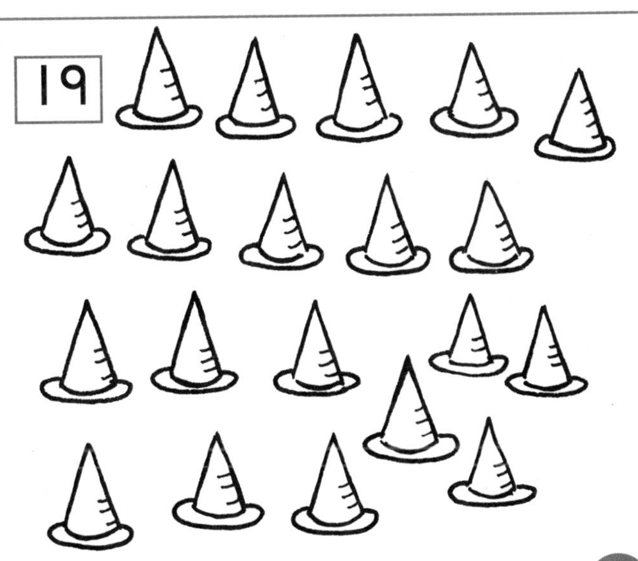

Missing numbers

Fill in the missing numbers.

1	2	3	4	5	6	7	8	9	10	11	12	13	14	15	16	17	18	19	20

Missing numbers

Fill in the missing numbers.

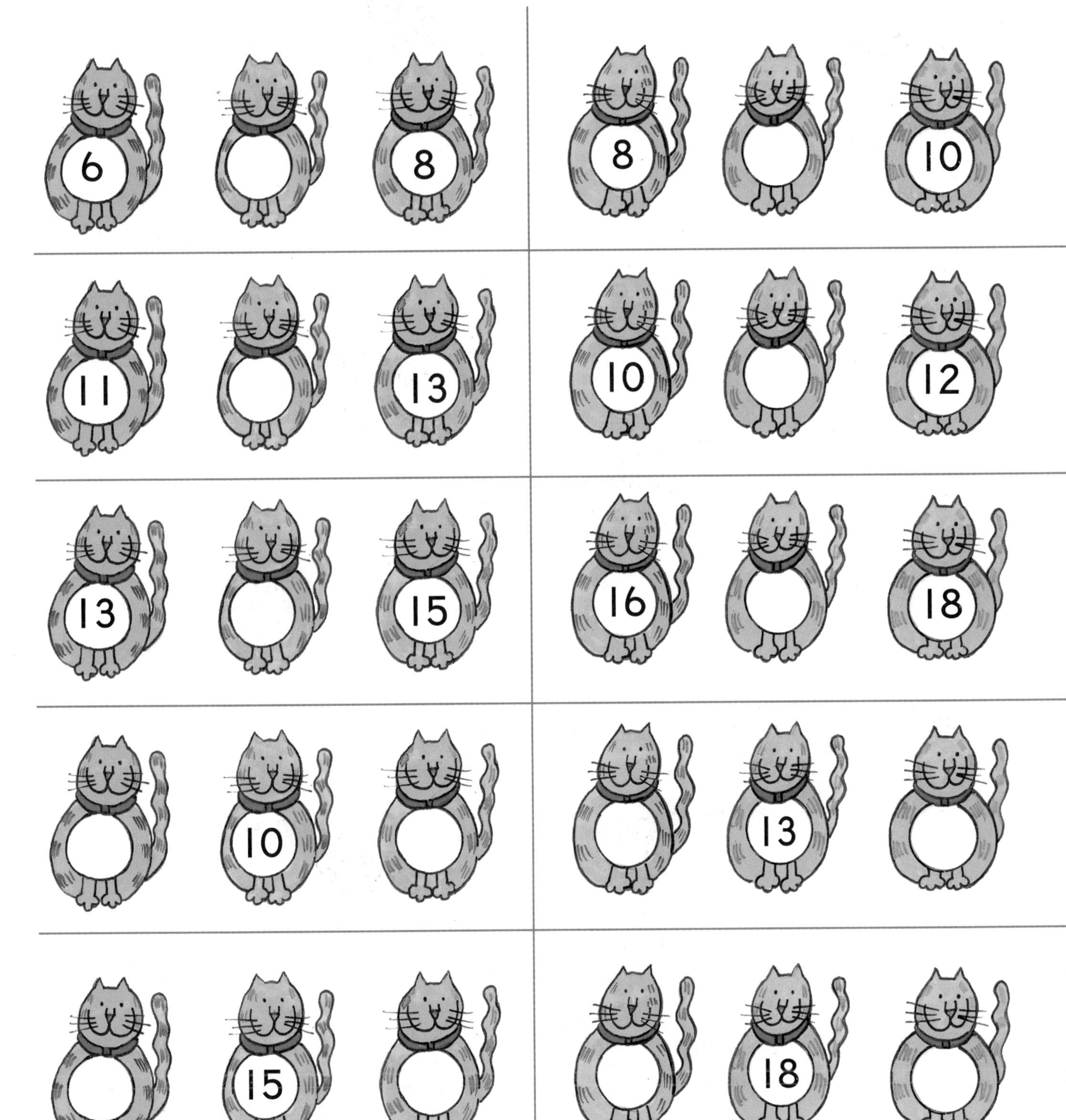

I to 20

Join the cat to the witch.

more less

Write

Who has the most books? ____________________

How many books has Pam? ____________________

Who has more books than Pam? ____________________

Who has less than 10 books? ____________________

____________________ has as many books as Pam.

Counting on two

Rabbit jumps forward 2 steps. Where does she land?

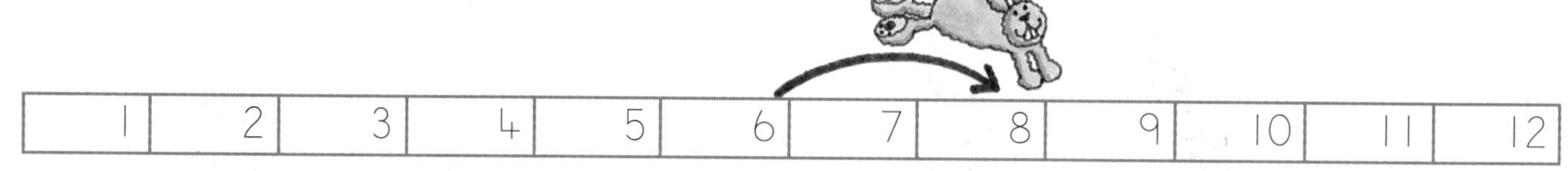

6 + 2 = ☐

1	2	3	4	5	6	7	8	9	10	11	12

8 + 2 = ☐

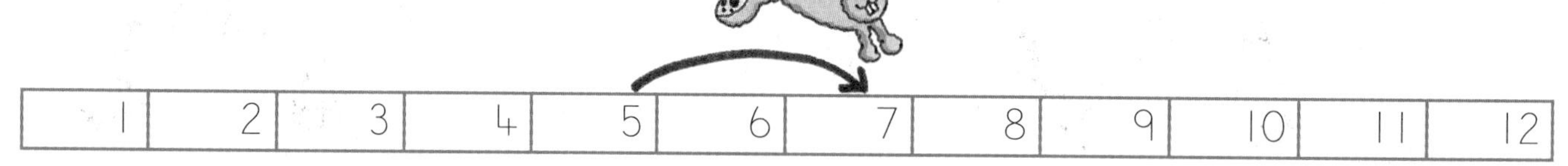

5 + 2 = ☐

1	2	3	4	5	6	7	8	9	10	11	12

10 + 2 = ☐

Now try these. Use your number strip.

5 + 1 = ☐	3 + 0 = ☐	7 + 1 = ☐	4 + 2 = ☐
9 + 0 = ☐	7 + 2 = ☐	9 + 1 = ☐	8 + 0 = ☐
6 + 1 = ☐	4 + 0 = ☐	8 + 1 = ☐	10 + 1 = ☐

Pairs

How many pairs can you make? Ring

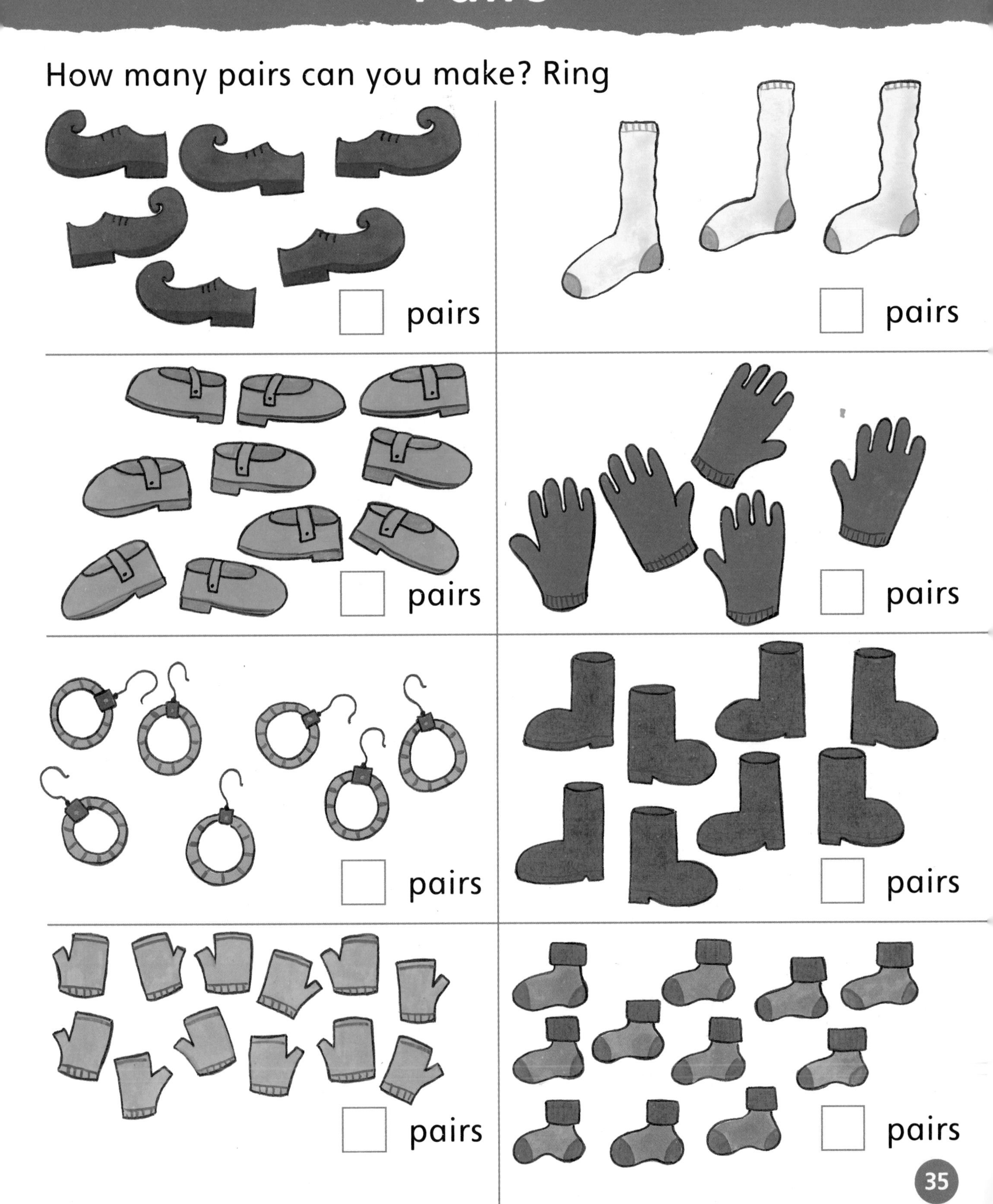

Even numbers

Count

Find the things that make up an even number and colour them.

Number stories: doubles

Tell the story. Write

4 + 4 = 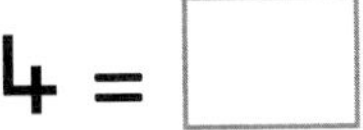

5 + 5 = ☐

3 + 3 = ☐

6 + 6 = ☐

Now try these. Use cubes.

7 + 7 = ☐ 8 + 8 = ☐ 9 + 9 = ☐ 10 + 10 = ☐

Number stories: near doubles

Write

3 + 2 = ☐

4 + 3 = ☐

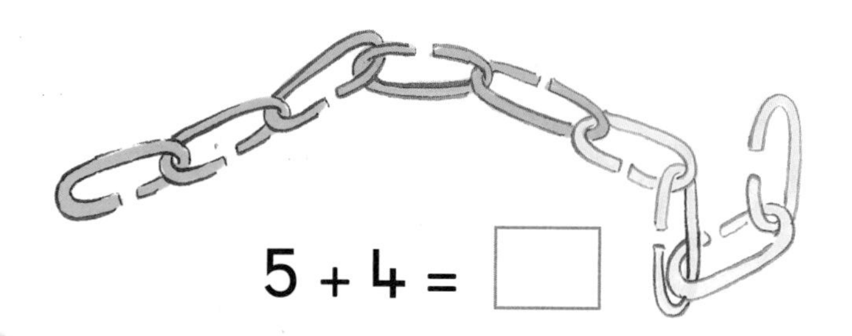

5 + 4 = ☐

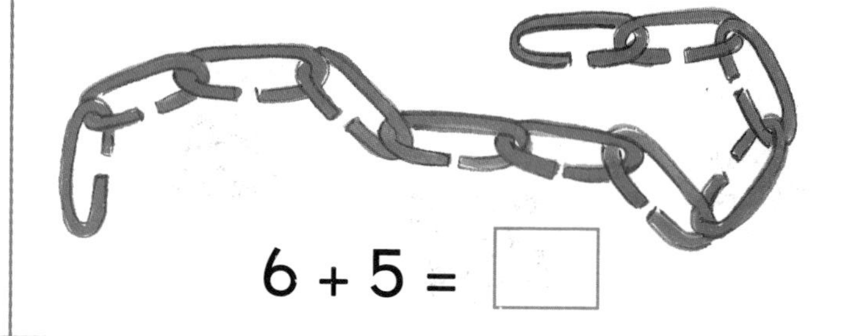

6 + 5 = ☐

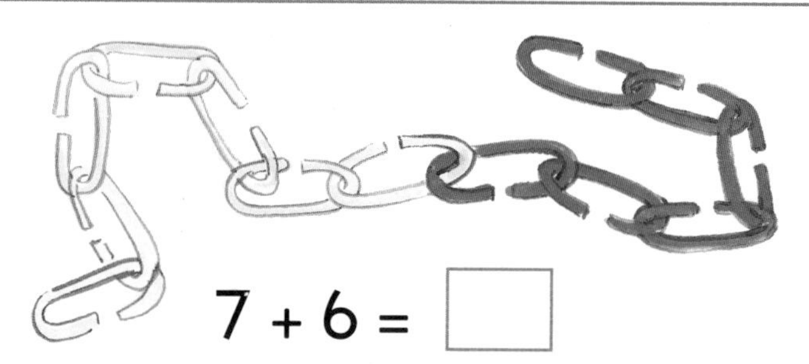

7 + 6 = ☐

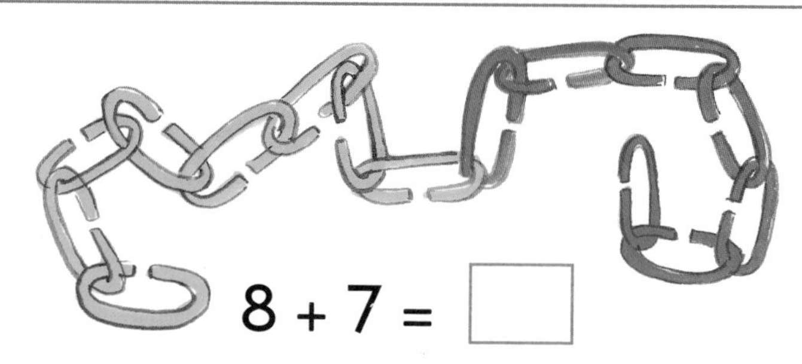

8 + 7 = ☐

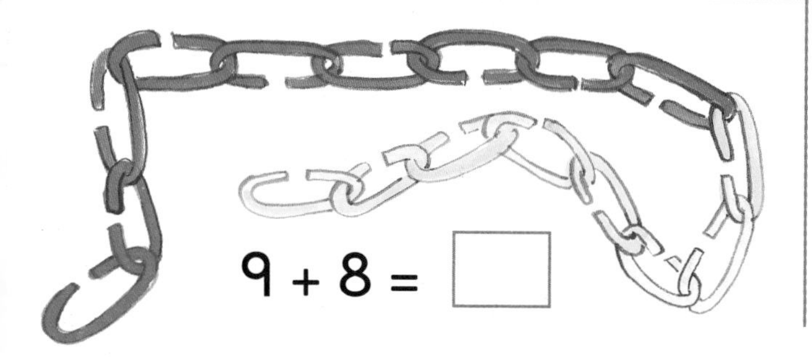

9 + 8 = ☐

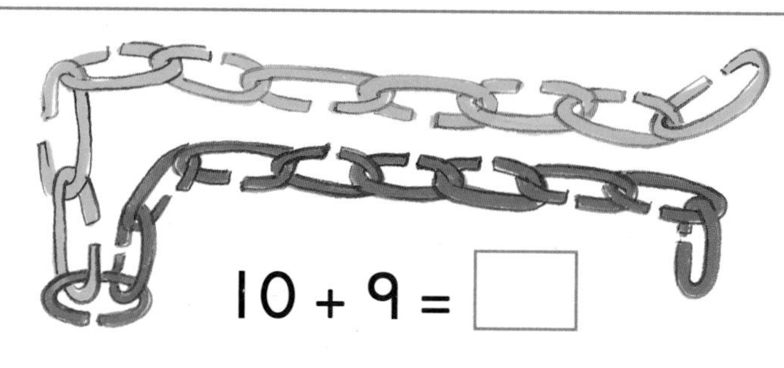

10 + 9 = ☐

Now try these. Use cubes.

4 + 5 = ☐ 6 + 7 = ☐ 5 + 6 = ☐

3 + 4 = ☐ 8 + 9 = ☐ 7 + 8 = ☐

Money

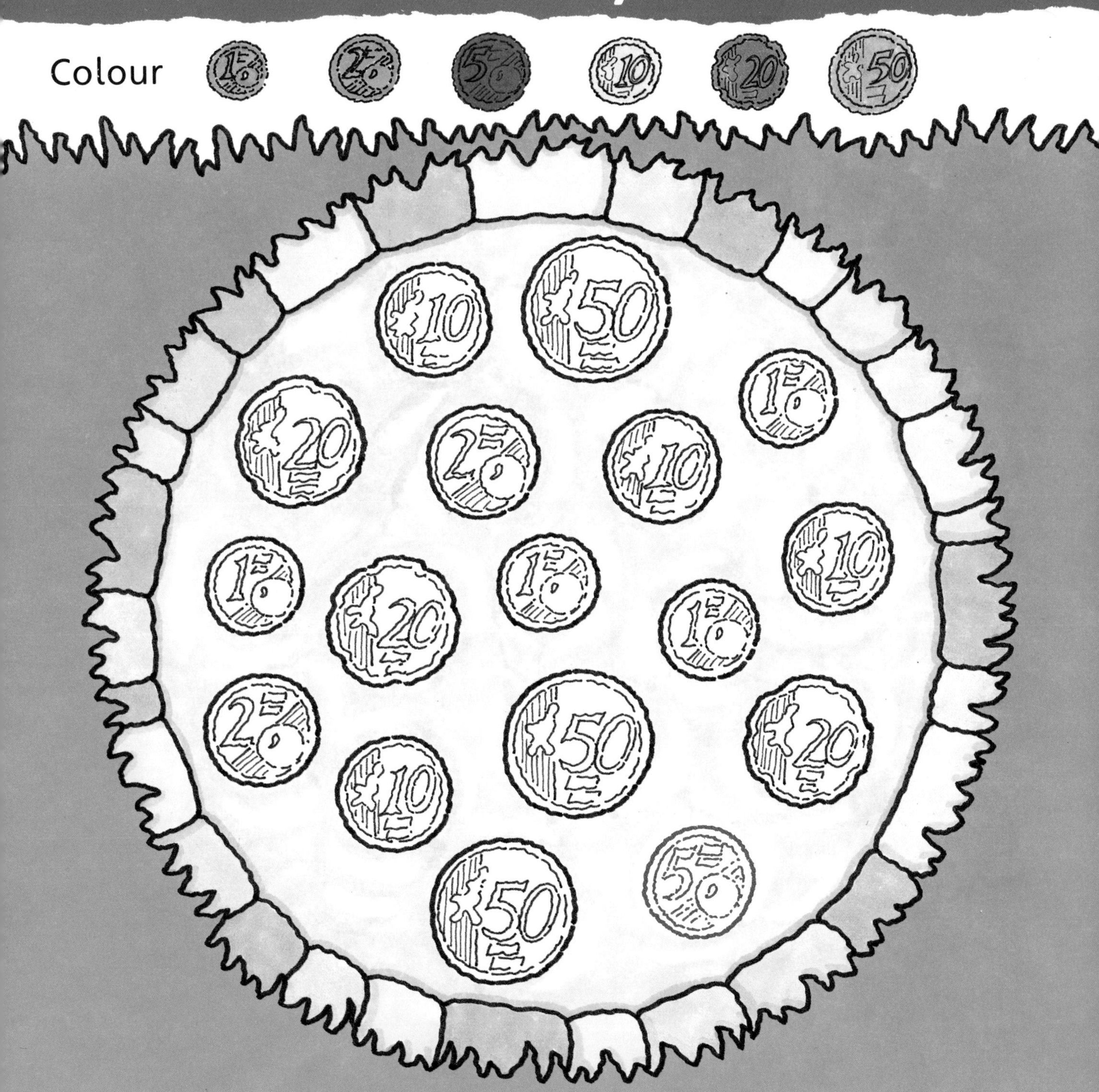

Kate put 7c in the well. What coins did she use?

Dan put 16c in the well. What coins did he use?

Money

Colour the coins.

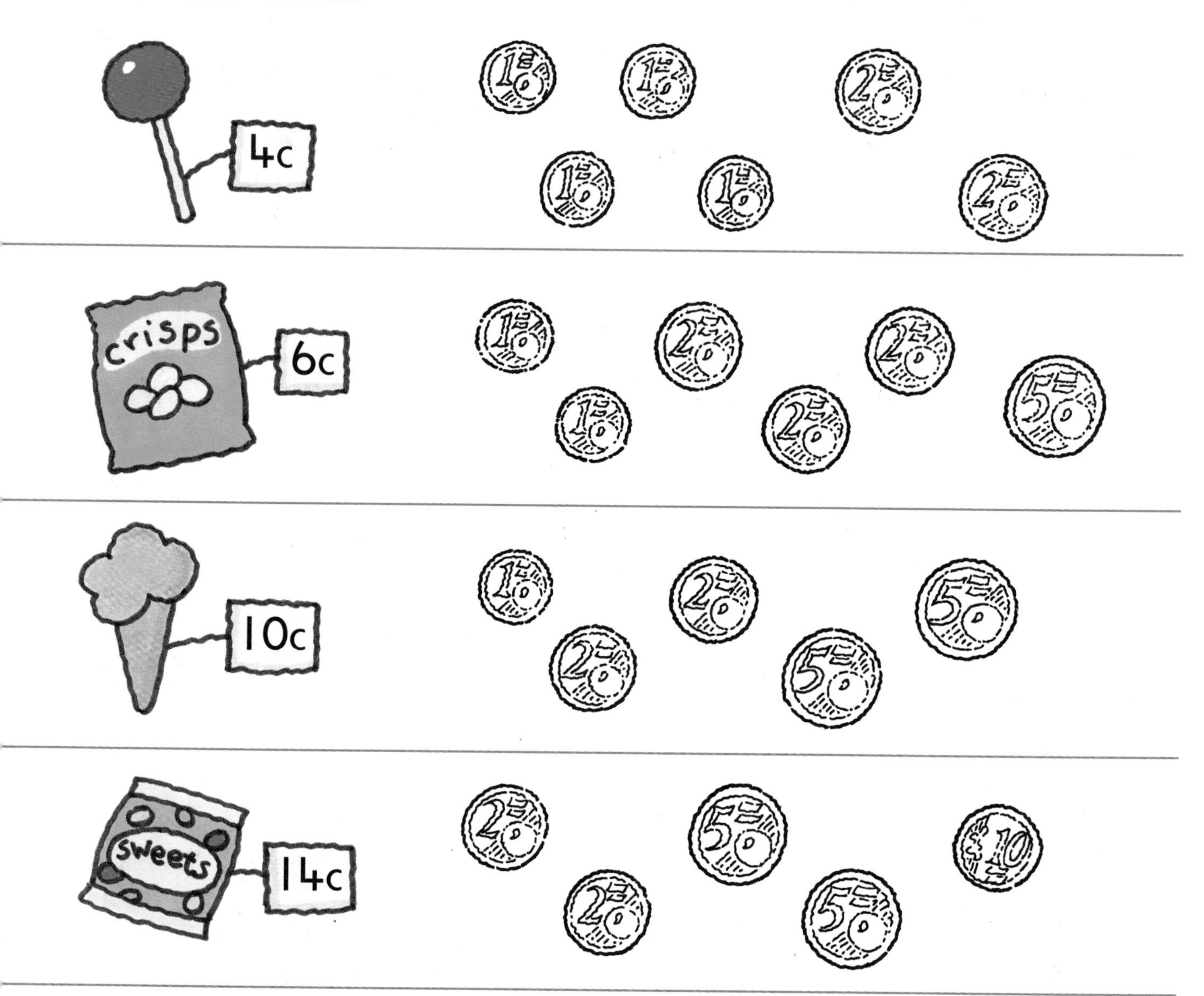

How many ways can you make 15c? Draw

Money

How much?

☐ + ☐ = ☐

 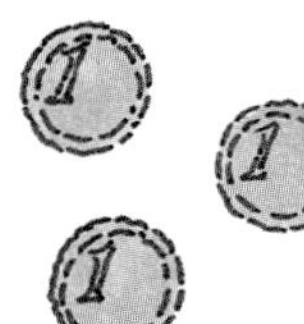

☐ + ☐ = ☐

☐ + ☐ = ☐

☐ + ☐ = ☐

☐ + ☐ = ☐

☐ + ☐ = ☐

Show and write.

Use 10c and 1c coins.

Number stories: subtraction

The magician is making people drop things.
Tell the story. Write

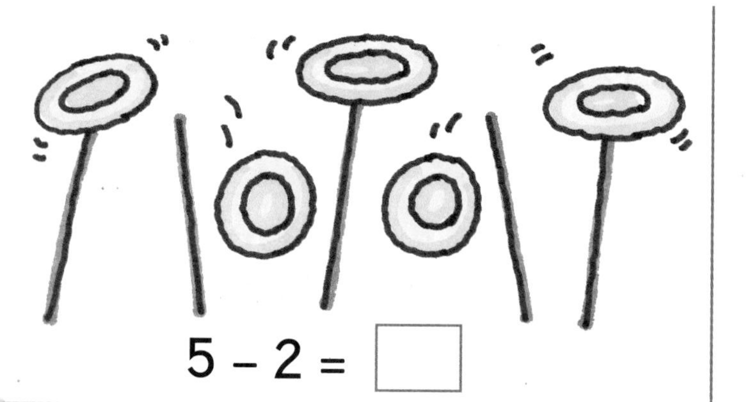

5 – 2 = ☐

7 – 1 = ☐

7 – 3 = ☐

9 – 2 = ☐

☐ – ☐ = ☐

☐ – ☐ = ☐

Draw your own number story.

Subtraction –

Write

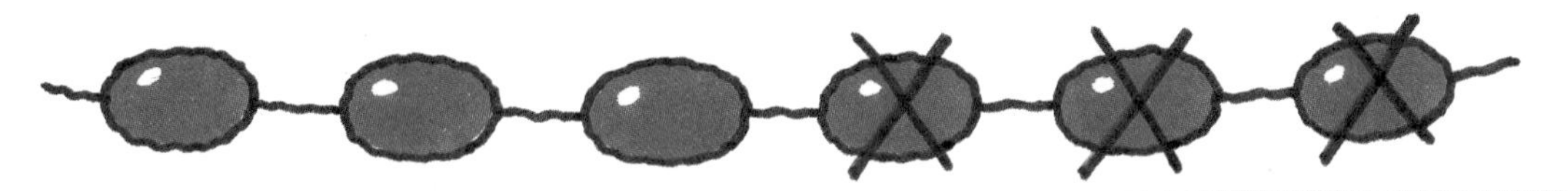

6 – 3 = ☐

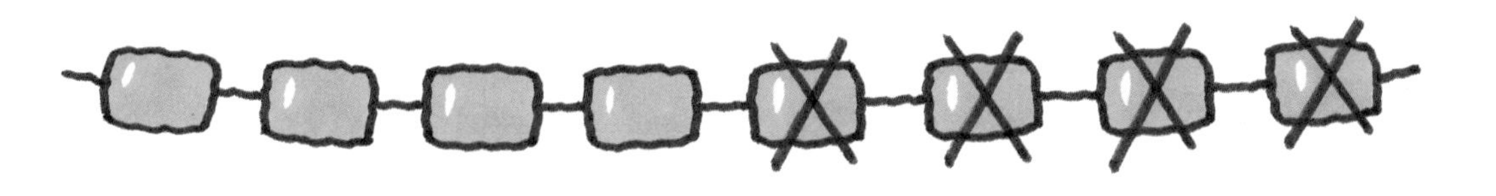

8 – 4 = ☐

☐ – ☐ = ☐

☐ – ☐ = ☐

☐ – ☐ = ☐

Draw

8 – 6 = ☐

7 – 7 = ☐

Counting back

Rabbit jumps back 1 step. Where does she land?

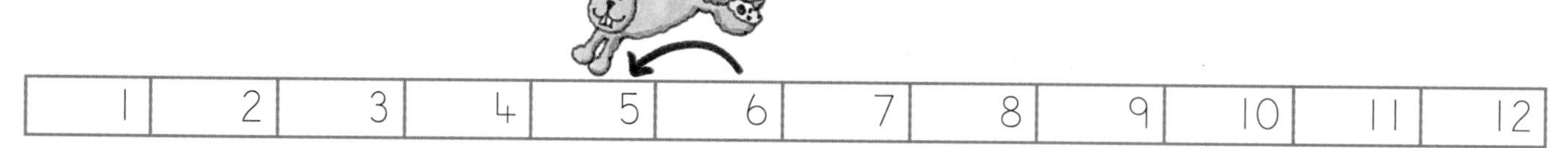

6 – 1 = ☐

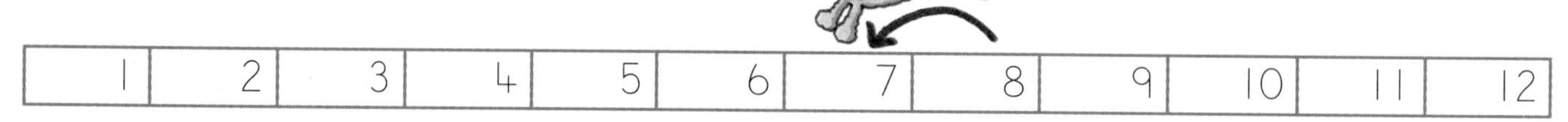

8 – 1 = ☐

Rabbit jumps back 2 steps. Where does she land?

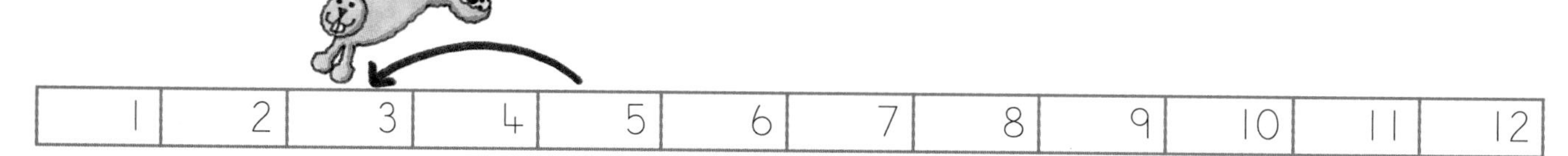

5 – 2 = ☐

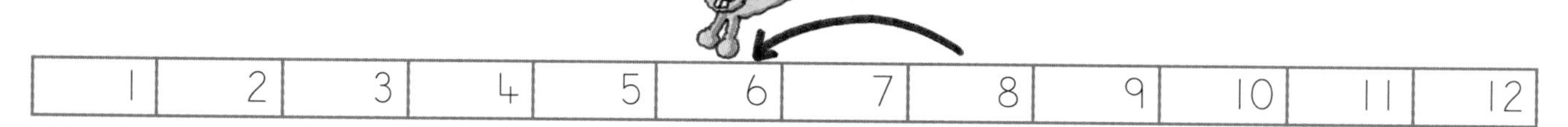

8 – 2 = ☐

Now try these. Use your number strip.

2 – 1 = ☐	5 – 1 = ☐	6 – 2 = ☐	4 – 2 = ☐
10 – 1 = ☐	4 – 1 = ☐	7 – 2 = ☐	3 – 2 = ☐
3 – 1 = ☐	7 – 1 = ☐	10 – 2 = ☐	9 – 2 = ☐

Subtract zero

The magician's rabbit only likes carrots.

4 – 0 = ☐

7 – 0 = ☐

5 – 0 = ☐

2 – 0 = ☐

9 – 0 = ☐

10 – 0 = ☐

Length

The wizard with the longest spell is the student of the week.

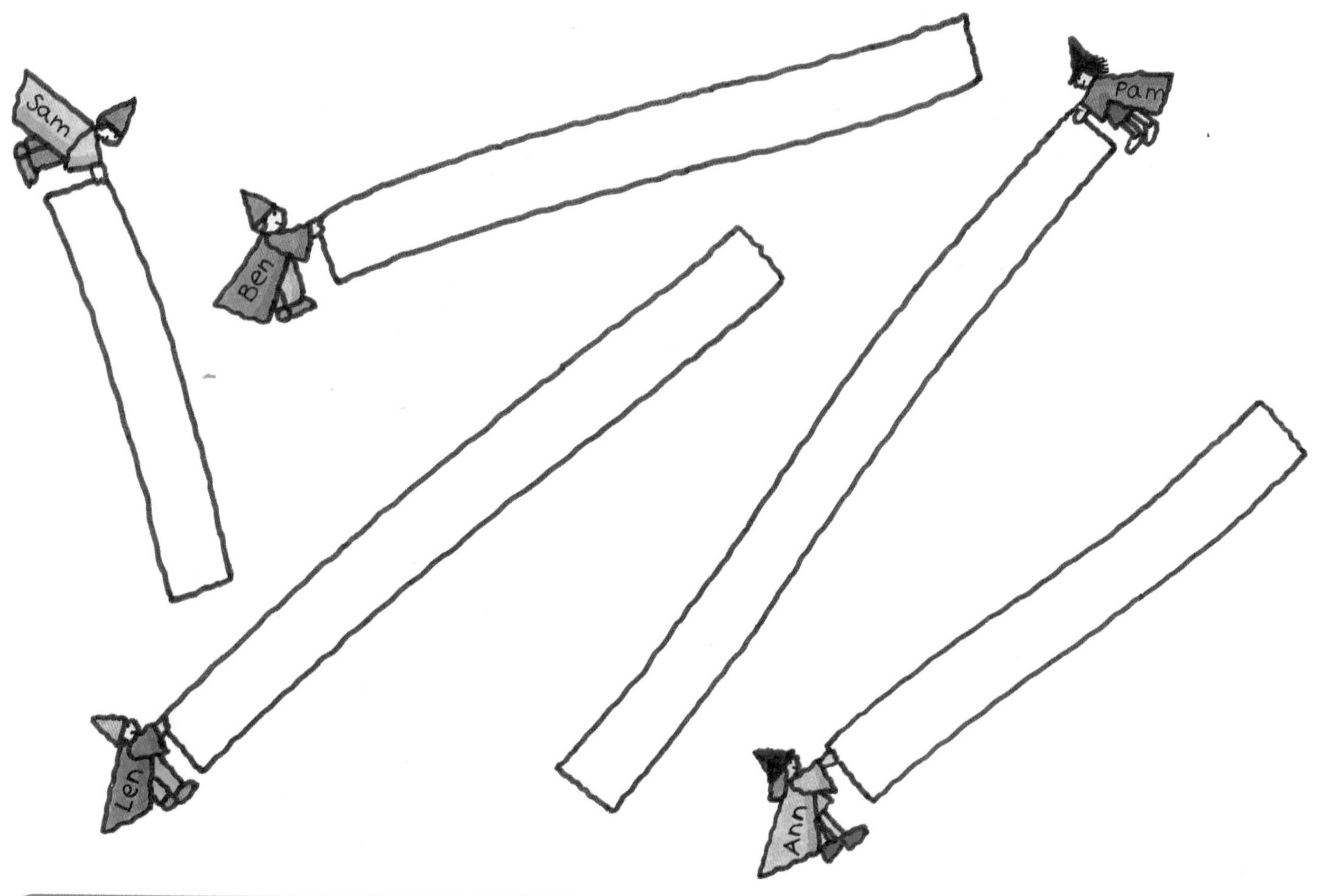

Who has the longest spell? ______________________

Who has the shortest spell? ______________________

Who has a longer spell than Ben? ______________________

Who has a shorter spell than Ann? ______________________

Order the spells from longest to shortest. ______________________

____

Length

How long are the magic wands? Use cubes.

Guess

Cubes

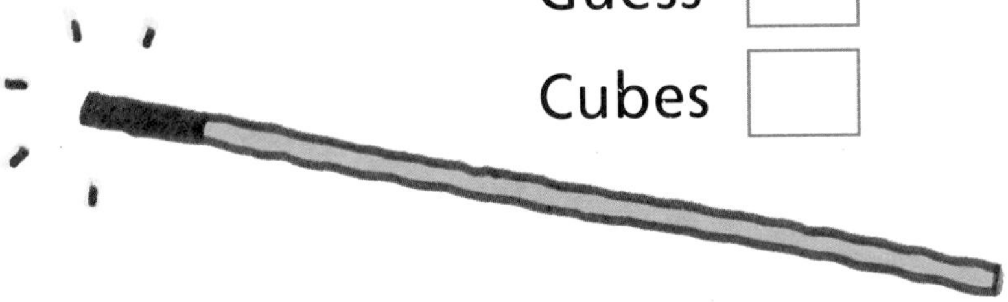

Guess

Cubes

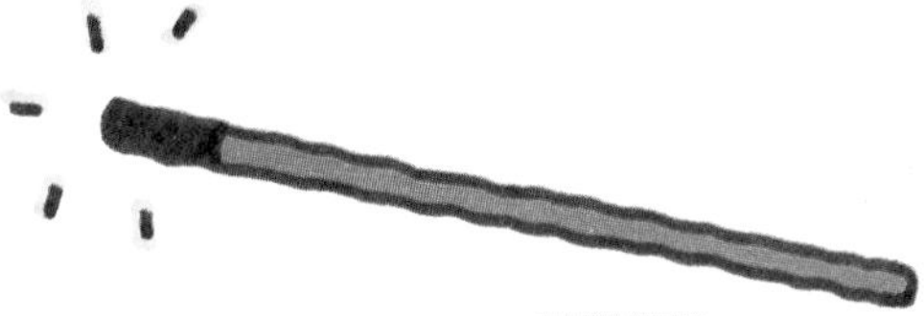

Guess

Cubes

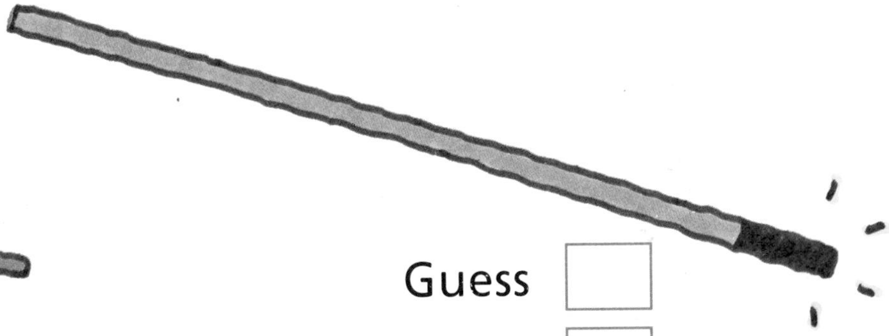

Guess

Cubes

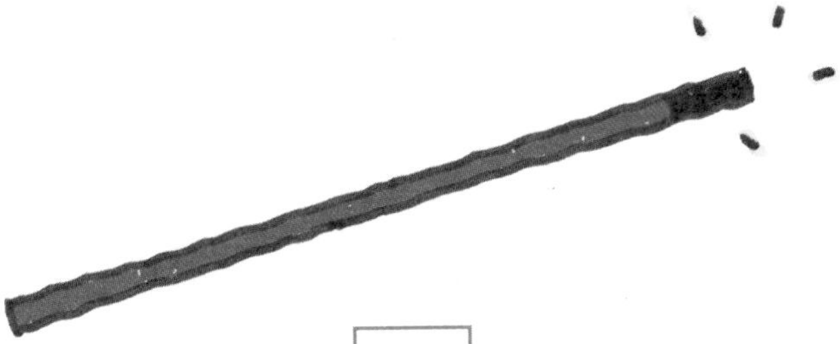

Guess

Cubes

Guess

Cubes

Length

Measure

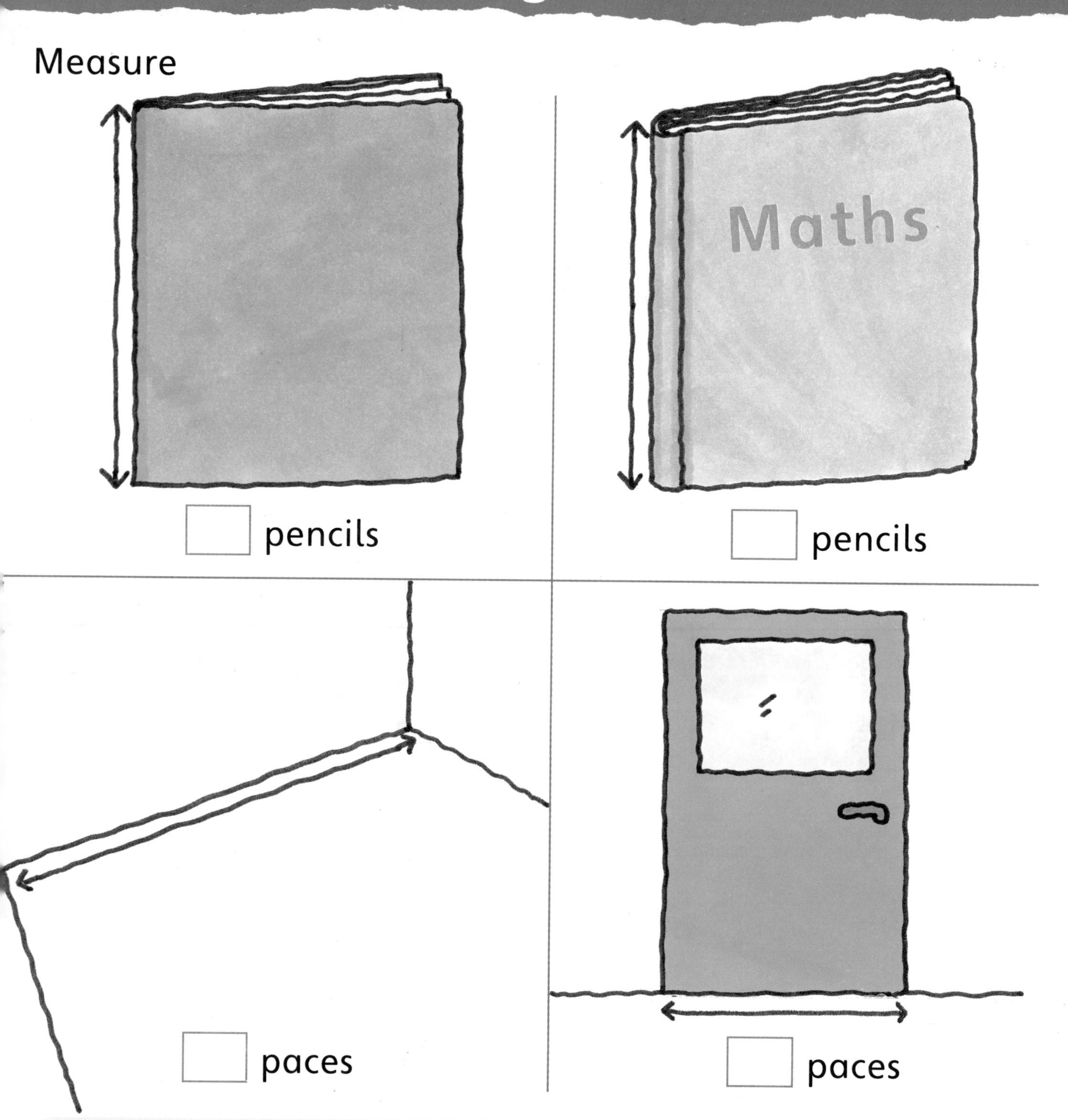

Measure other things in your classroom using pencils or paces.

The metre

Find and draw things in your classroom that are about a metre.

A metre always stays the same.

Find and draw things that are more than a metre.
Find and draw things that are less than a metre.

Counting in tens

Count

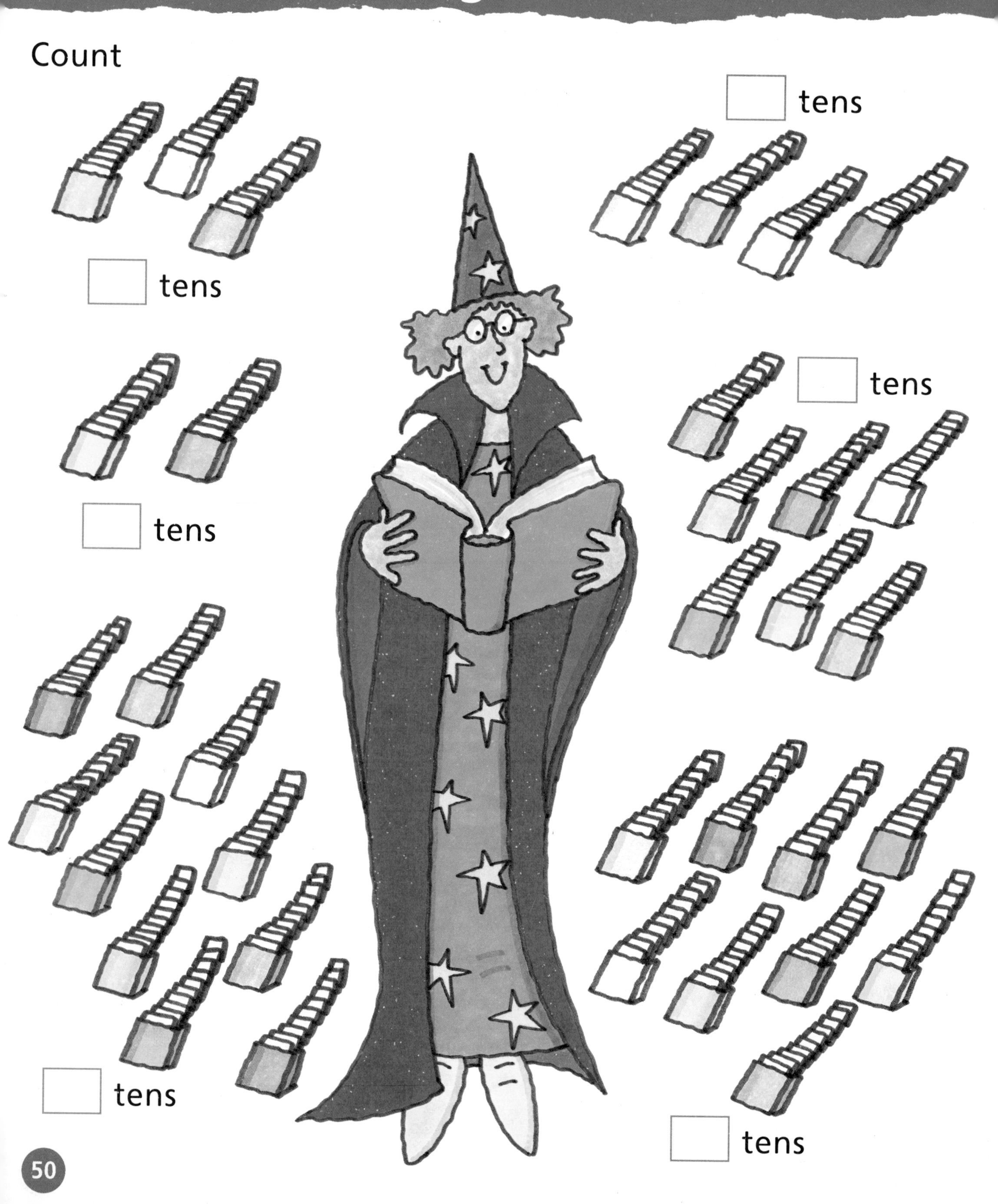

Counting in tens

How many?

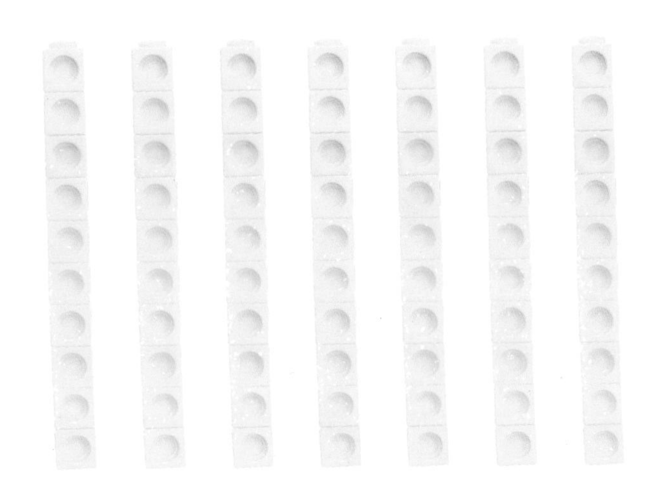

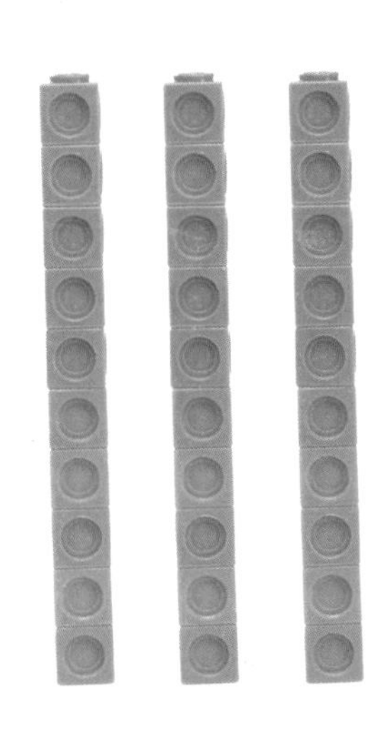

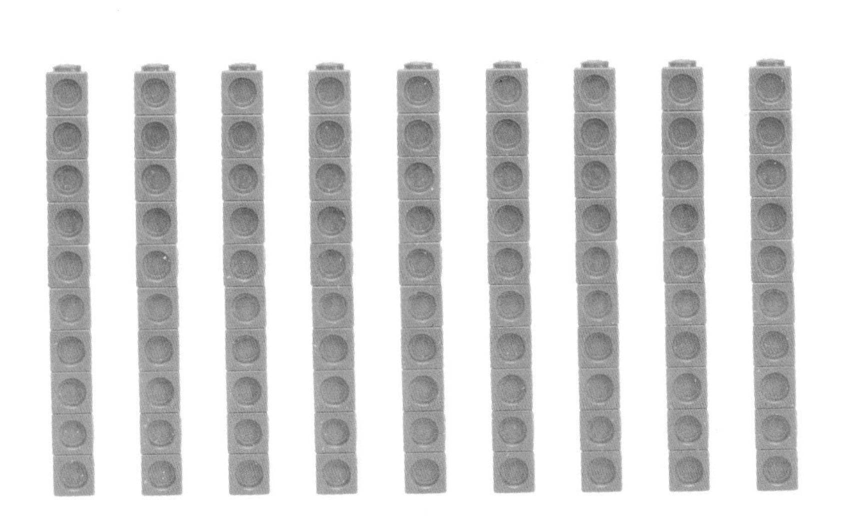

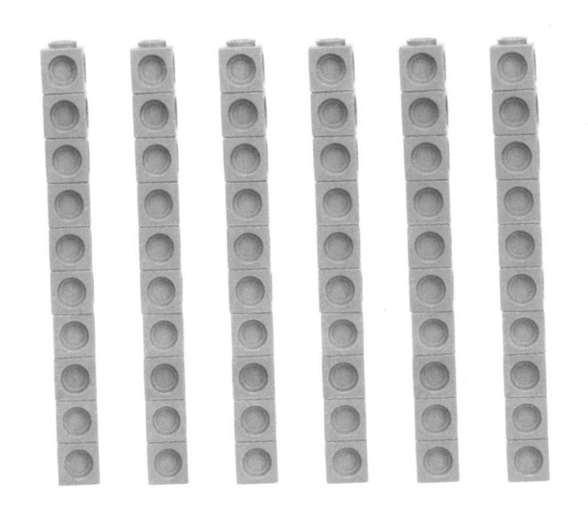

☐ tens

☐ tens

☐ tens

☐ tens

☐ tens

Counting in tens

The witches are counting their spell books.
Help them to count.

60
70
80
90
100
10

Counting in tens

Ring and colour.

30

50

40

90

100

80

Think
Talk

Shape

Colour

Shape

Help the clown to sort the shapes. Draw and colour.

4 sides	3 sides	1 curved side

Shape

Colour ▢ ▭ △ ○ ◗ and count.

Number stories: subtraction

Tell the story. Write

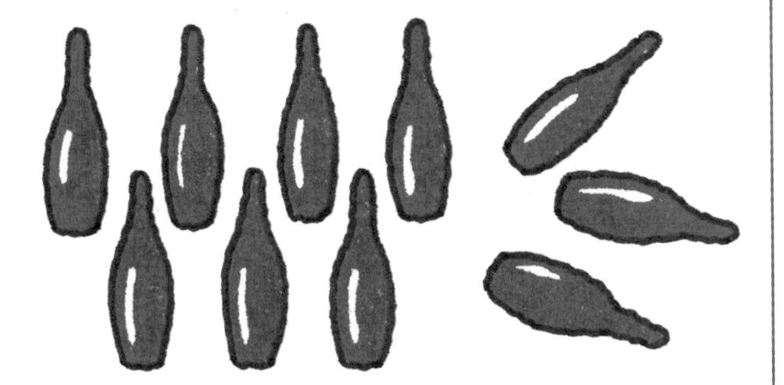

10 – 3 = ☐

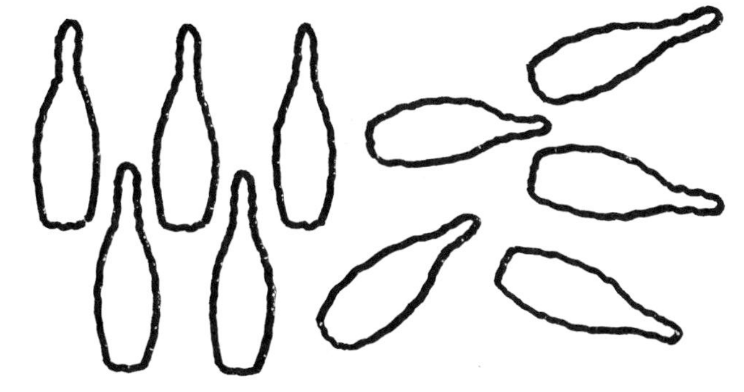

10 – 5 = ☐

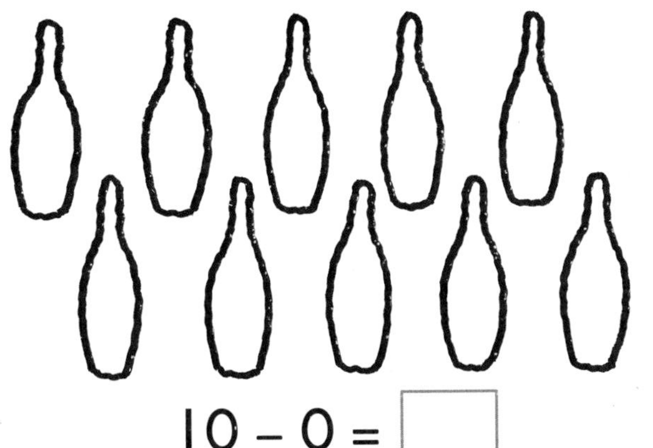

10 – 0 = ☐

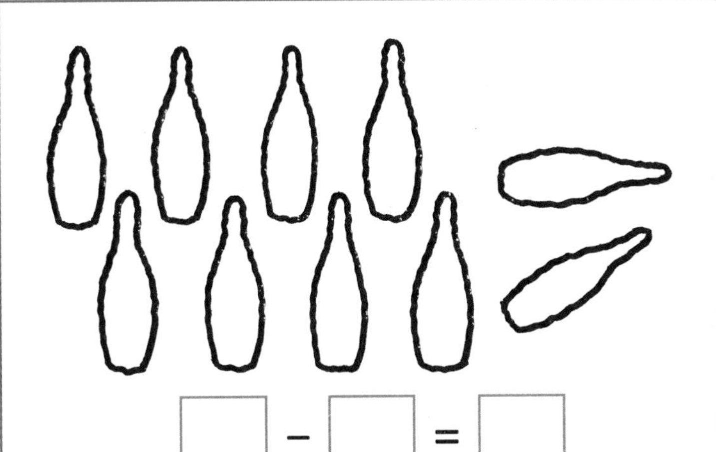

☐ – ☐ = ☐

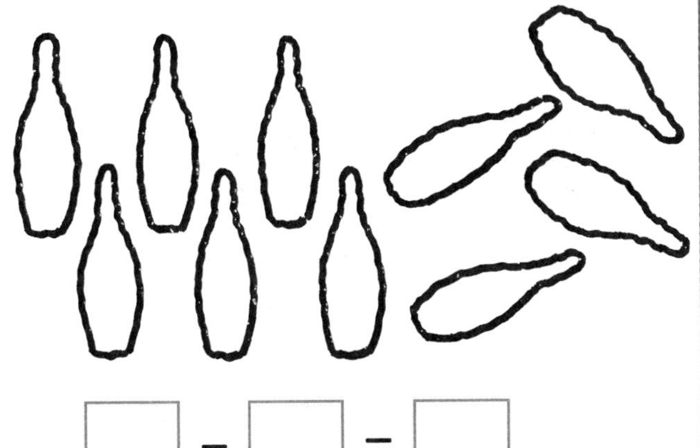

☐ – ☐ = ☐

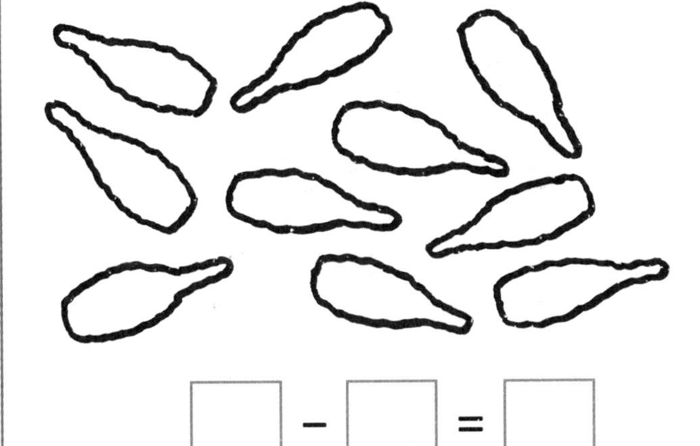

☐ – ☐ = ☐

Draw and write other stories about 10 skittles.

Make ten

Each star makes ten. Write the missing number.

Draw stars that make eight.

Who has more?

Jess the juggler and Rolo the clown are counting everything before the show. Tell the story. Write

Rolo has ☐ skittles.

Jess has ☐ skittles.

_______ has ☐ more.

Rolo has ☐ dice.

Jess has ☐ dice.

_______ has ☐ more.

Rolo has ☐ bow-ties.

Jess has ☐ bow-ties.

_______ has ☐ more.

Rolo has ☐ hats.

Jess has ☐ hats.

_______ has ☐ more.

Tell and write other stories. Use cubes.

above below

Draw
above
below
above
below
above
below
above
below
above
below
above
below

Addition: three numbers

Add

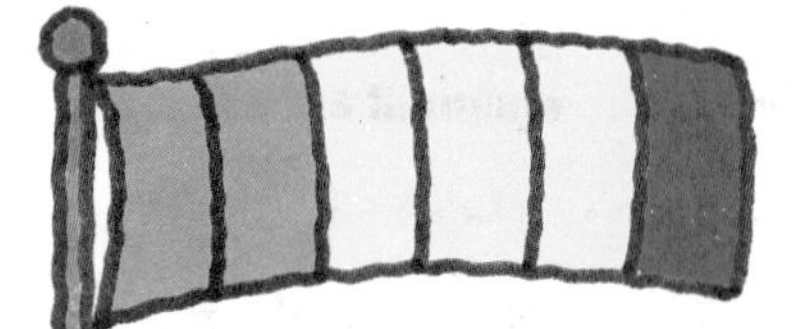

2 + 3 + 1 =

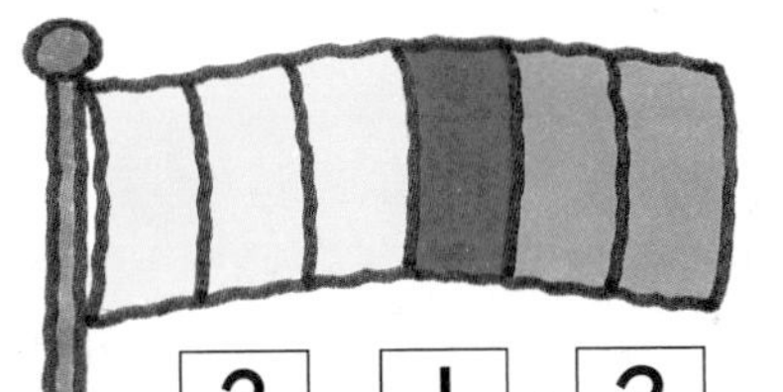

3 + 1 + 2 =

4 + 3 + 2 =

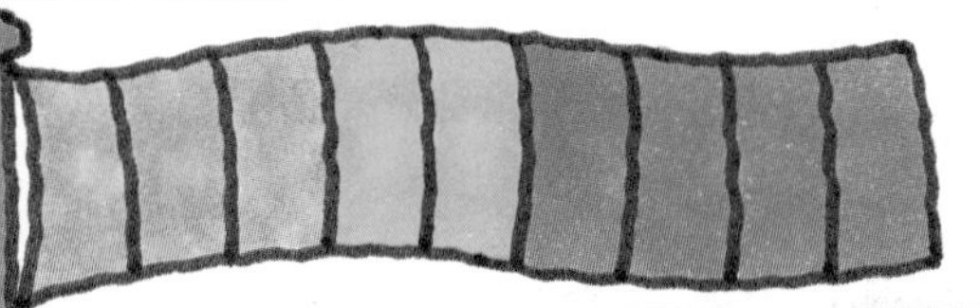

3 + 2 + 4 =

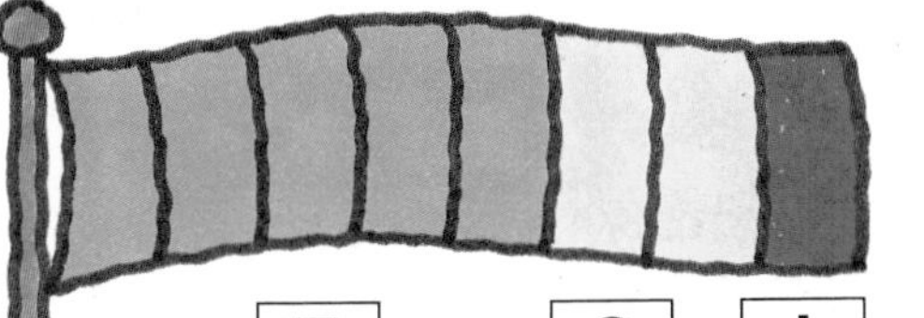

5 + 2 + 1 =

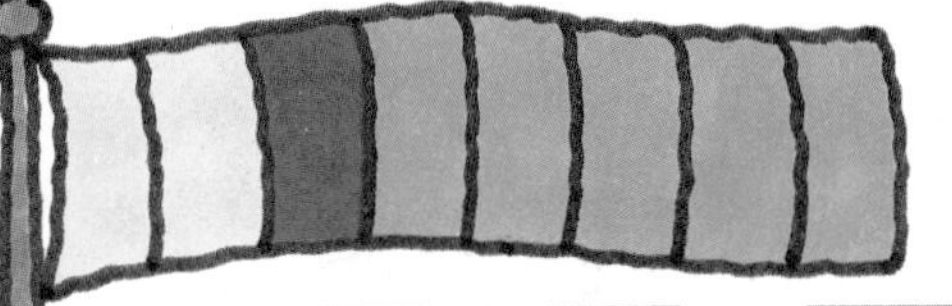

2 + 1 + 5 =

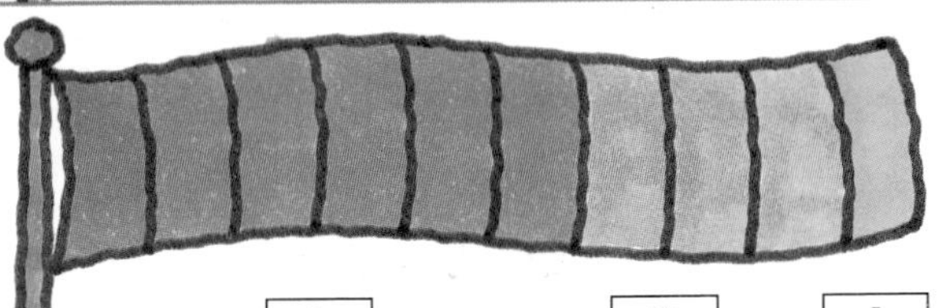

6 + 3 + 1 =

3 + 1 + 6 =

Now try these. Use cubes.

4 + 5 + 1 =

3 + 3 + 2 =

6 + 4 + 2 =

5 + 3 + 4 =

7 + 7 + 1 =

6 + 5 + 2 =

2 + 4 + 5 =

4 + 3 + 4 =

5 + 3 + 3 =

Ten frame

Draw and write.

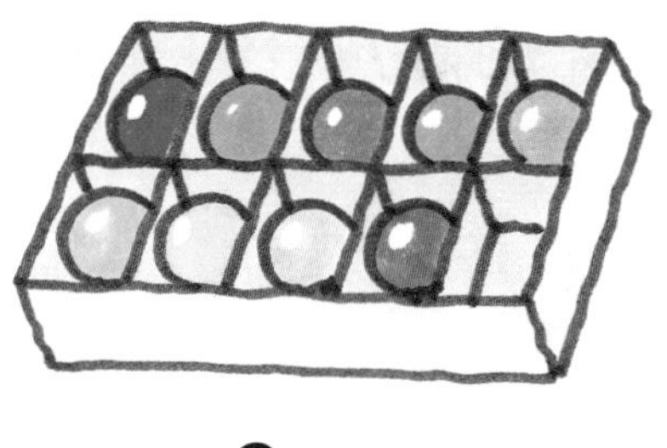
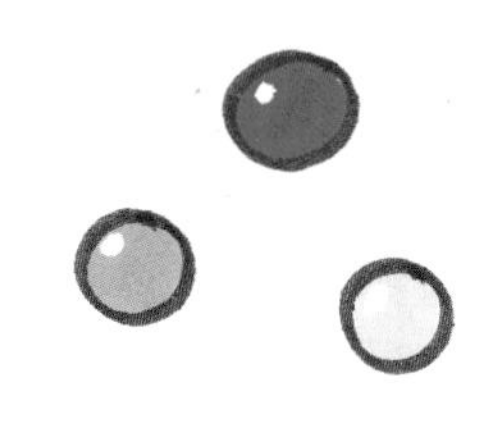

9 + 3 = ☐

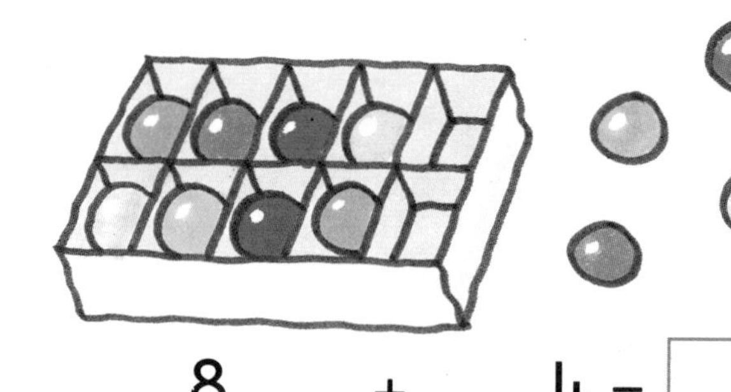

8 + 4 = ☐

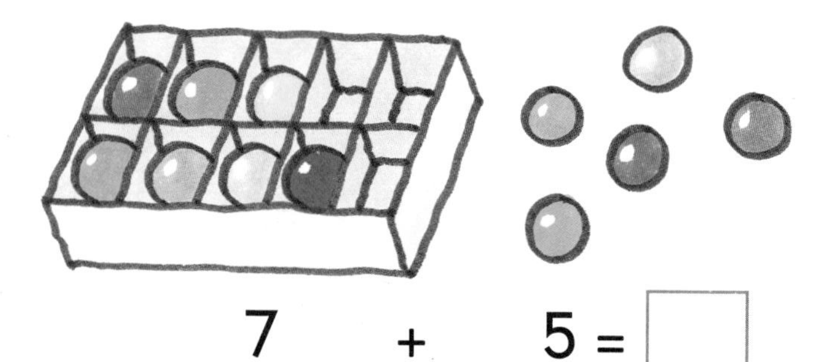

7 + 5 = ☐

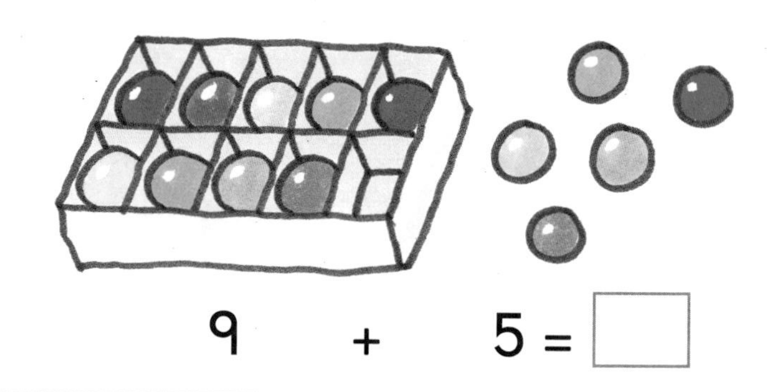

9 + 5 = ☐

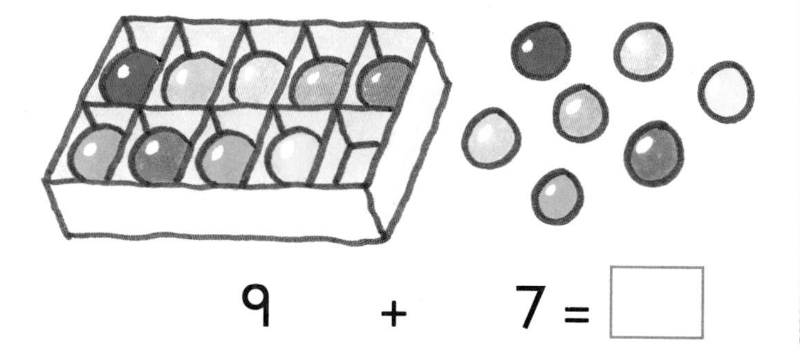

9 + 7 = ☐

8 + 3 = ☐

Now try these. Use counters and ten frames.

8 + 5 = ☐	9 + 4 = ☐	8 + 6 = ☐
7 + 6 = ☐	9 + 6 = ☐	10 + 7 = ☐
7 + 4 = ☐	10 + 5 = ☐	9 + 8 = ☐

Counting on

Use the numberline. Add

1	2	3	4	5	6	7	8	9	10	11	12	13	14	15	16	17	18	19	20

$4 + 3 = \square$ $9 + 4 = \square$ $6 + 9 = \square$

$7 + 7 = \square$ $8 + 9 = \square$ $8 + 8 = \square$

$6 + 5 = \square$ $7 + 3 = \square$ $8 + 7 = \square$

$9 + 2 = \square$ $8 + 4 = \square$ $9 + 3 = \square$

$6 + 4 = \square$ $6 + 6 = \square$ $6 + 7 = \square$

$7 + 5 = \square$ $6 + 8 = \square$ $8 + 3 = \square$

$7 + 9 = \square$ $8 + 5 = \square$ $9 + 6 = \square$

Half

Colour half of these shapes.

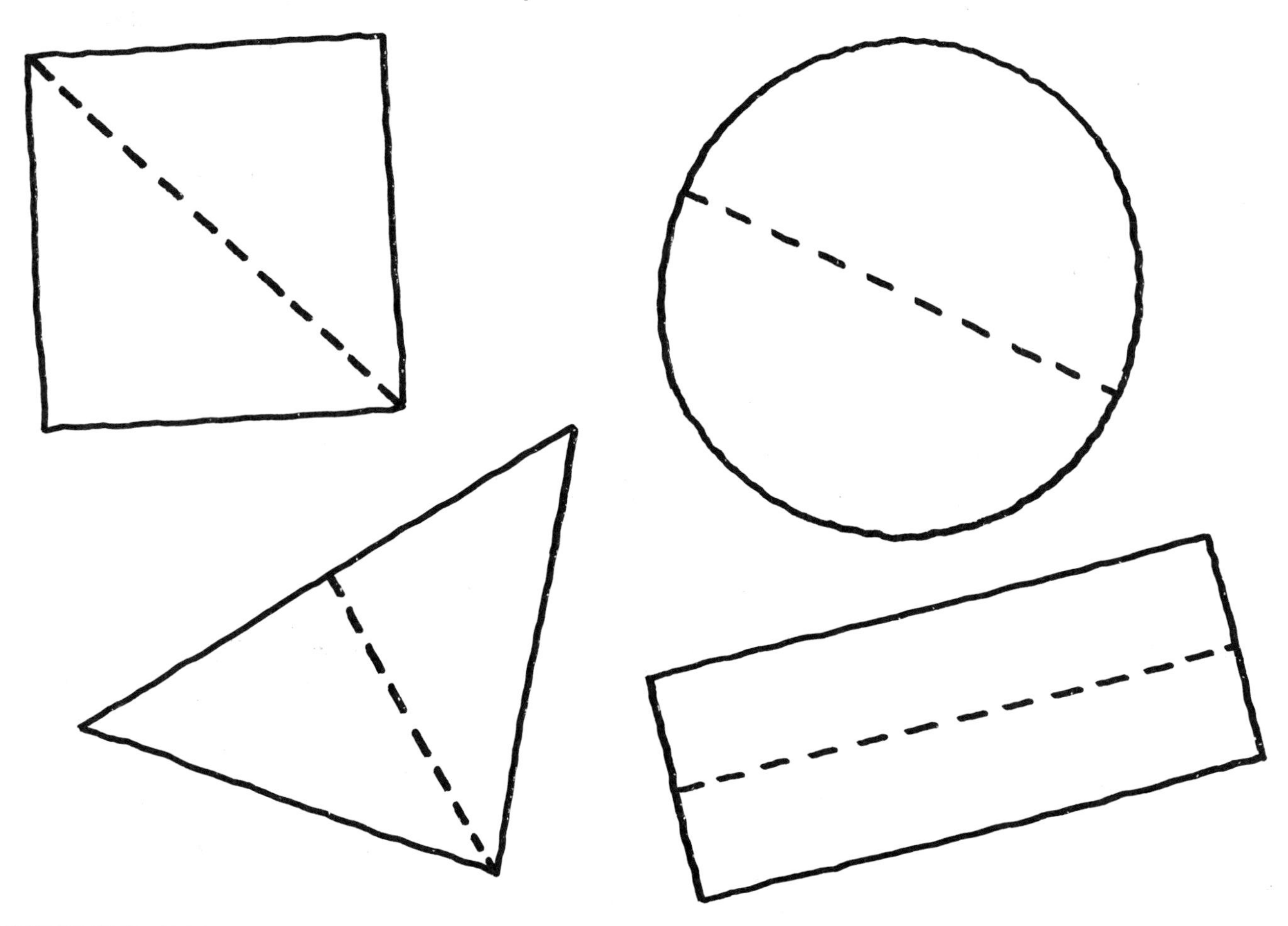

How many other ways can you fold the shapes in half?

Half

Colour one half.

Ring the things that have only one half coloured.

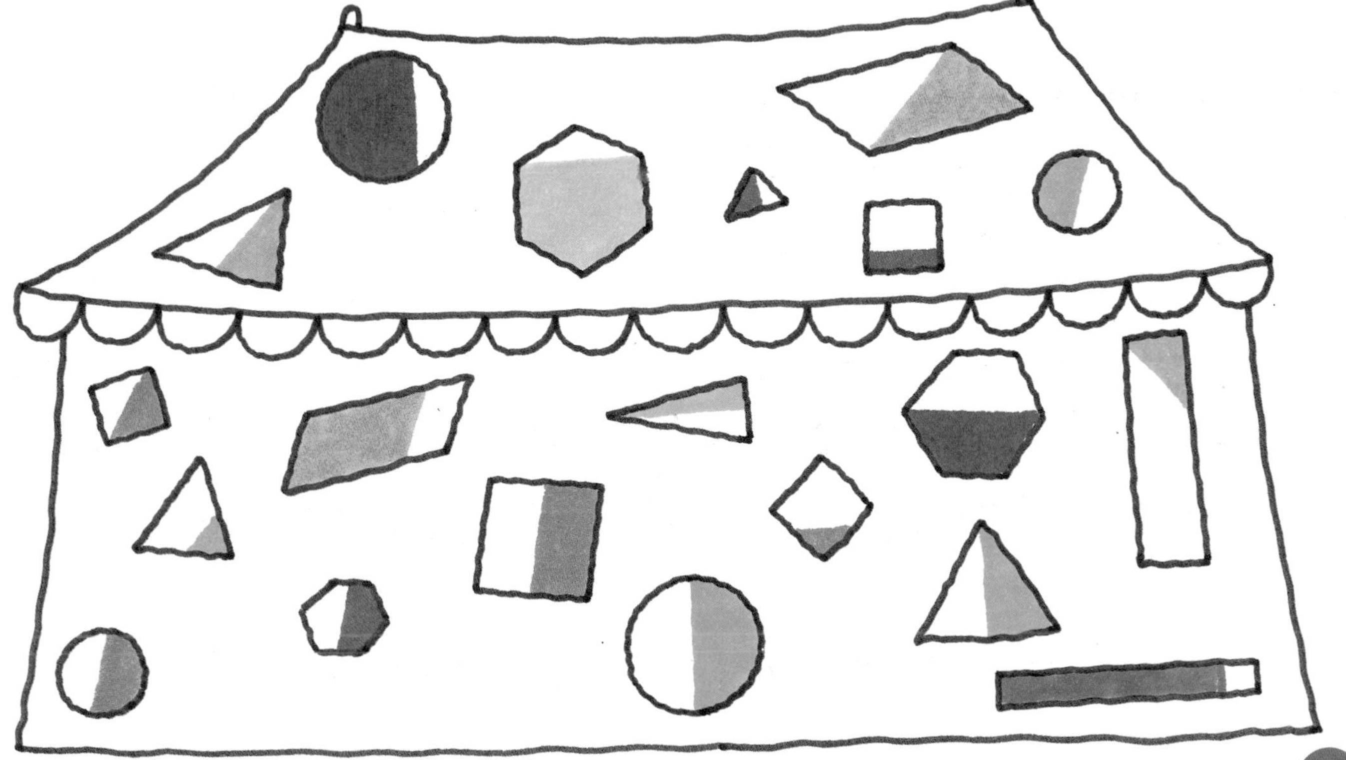

Pattern

Extend the pattern.

Make your own pattern.

Shape

Help the clown to sort the shapes. How many?

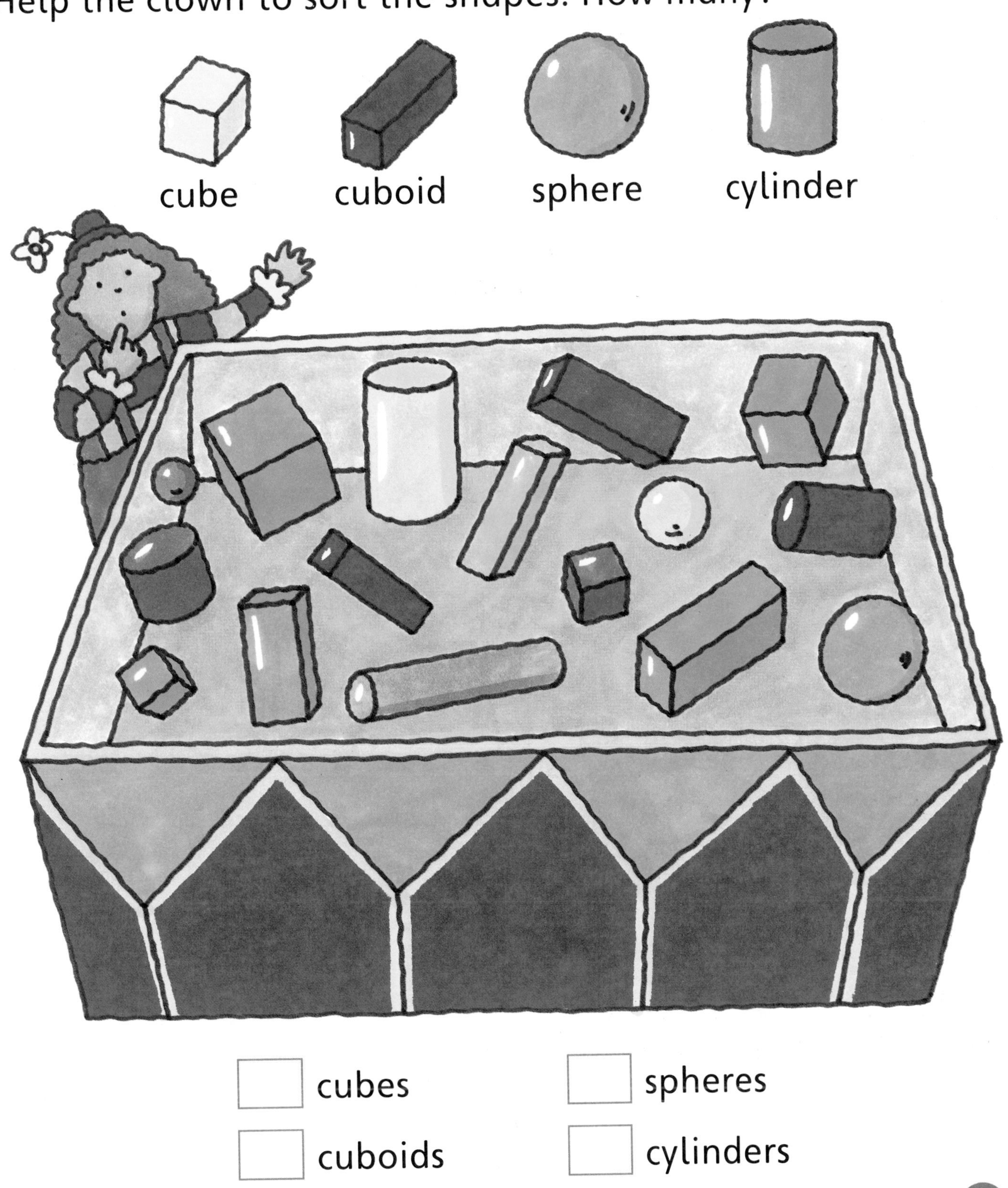

☐ cubes ☐ spheres

☐ cuboids ☐ cylinders

Shape

What things roll? Match the shapes to the hoops.

Shape

Colour the flat faces blue and the curved faces orange.

How many?

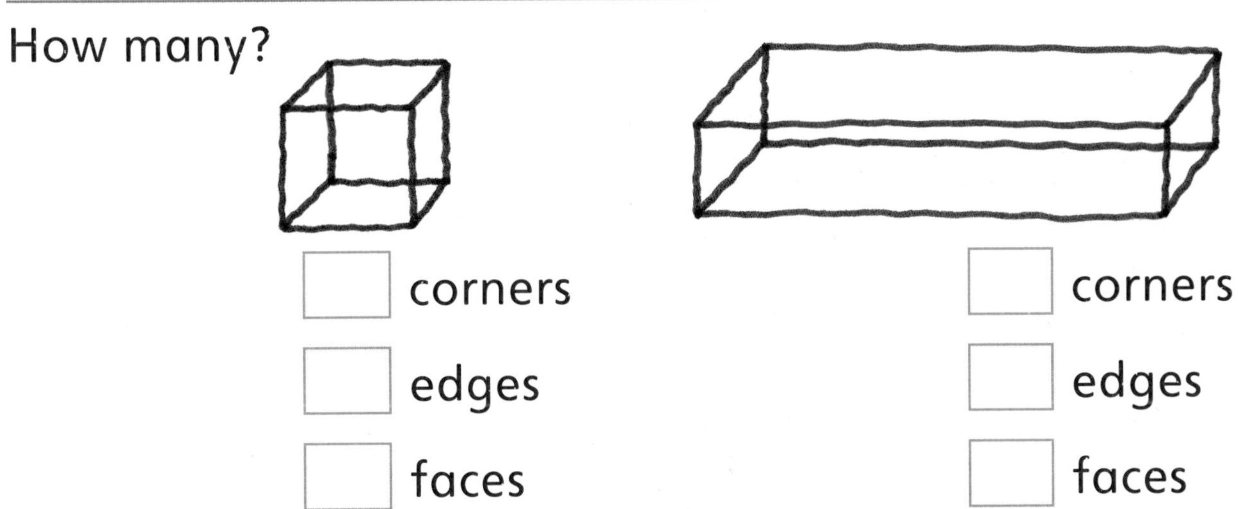

☐ corners	☐ corners
☐ edges	☐ edges
☐ faces	☐ faces

Grouping in tens

How many bags of ten balls are there?
How many balls are left over?

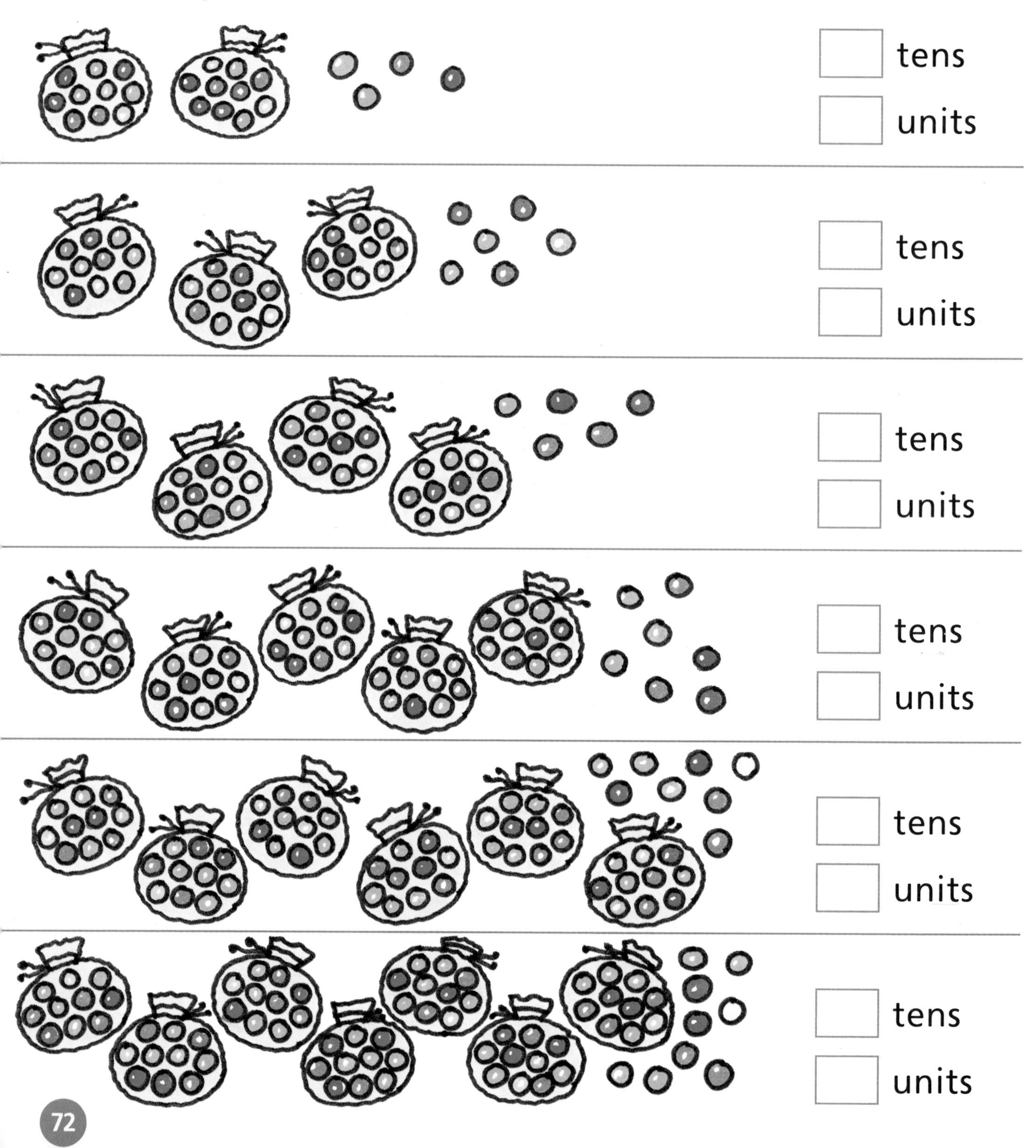

Grouping in tens

How many bundles of ten are there?
How many skittles are left over?

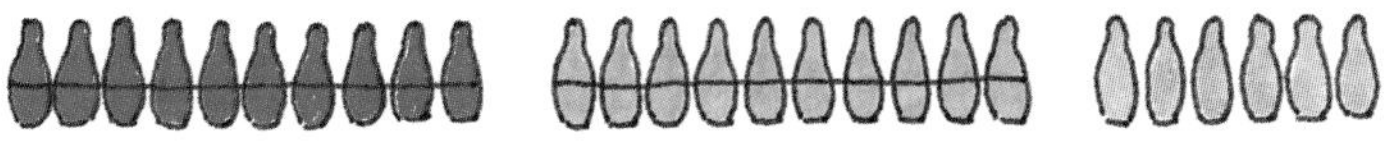

☐ tens ☐ units

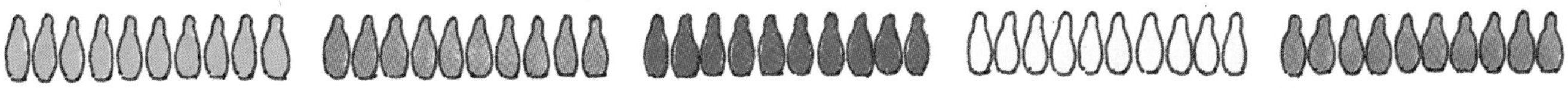

☐ tens ☐ units

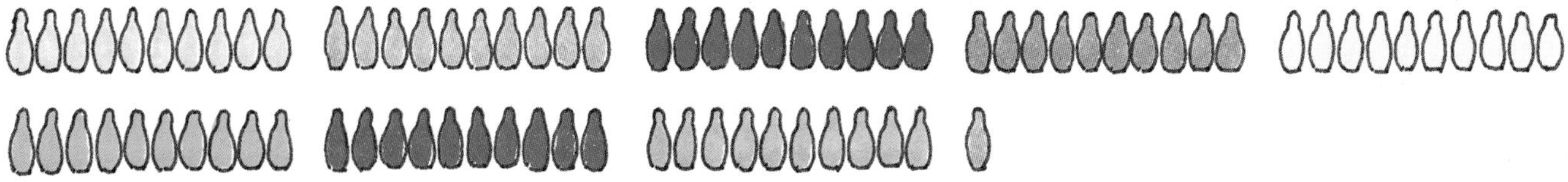

☐ tens ☐ units

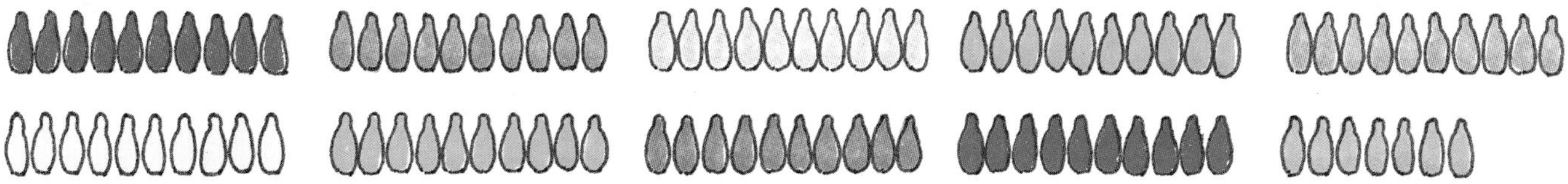

☐ tens ☐ units

Make these numbers. Use straws or lollipop sticks.

32 59 61 48 27 83 94 77 65 86

Grouping in tens

How many?

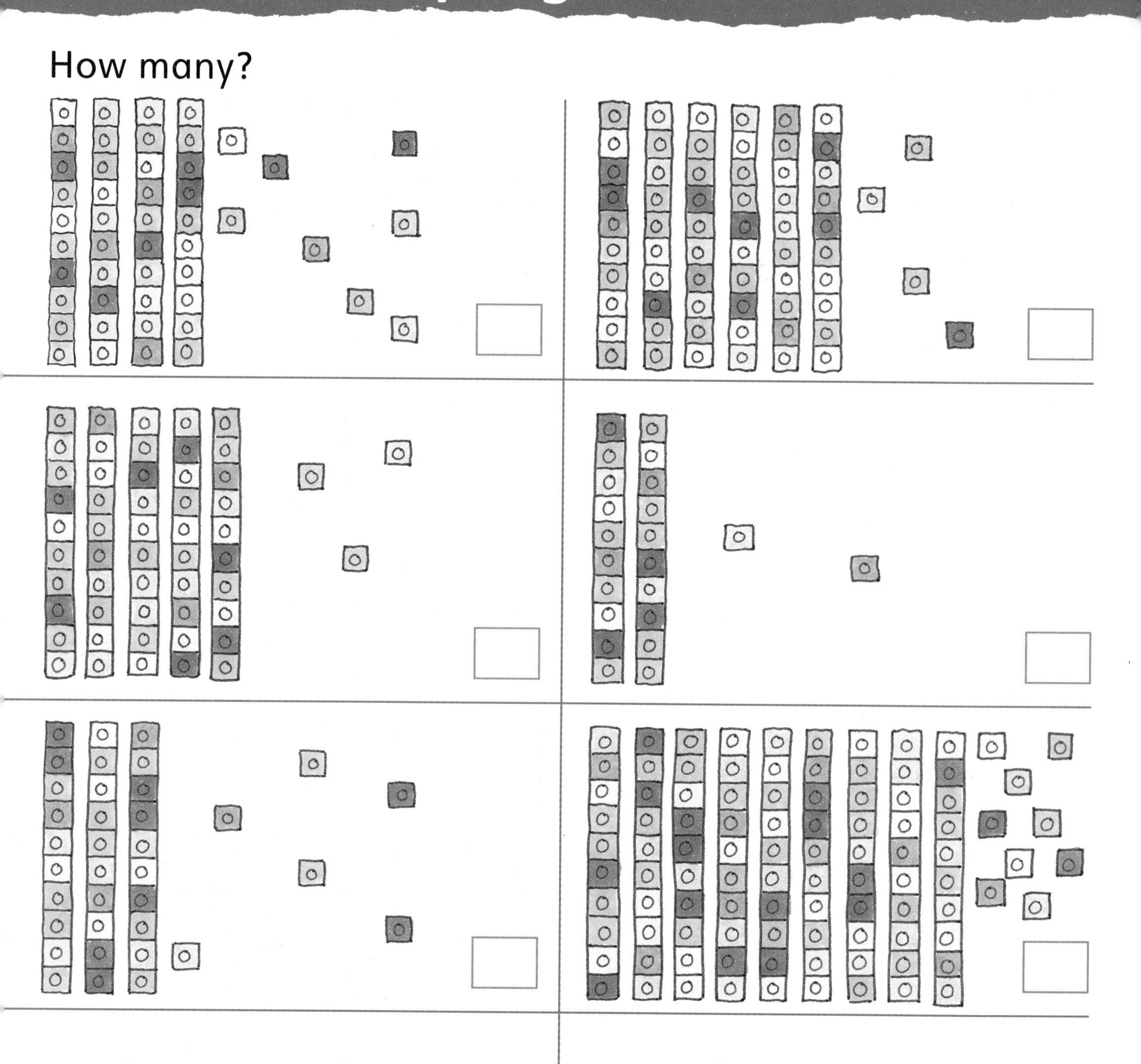

29

32

Grouping in tens

Colour

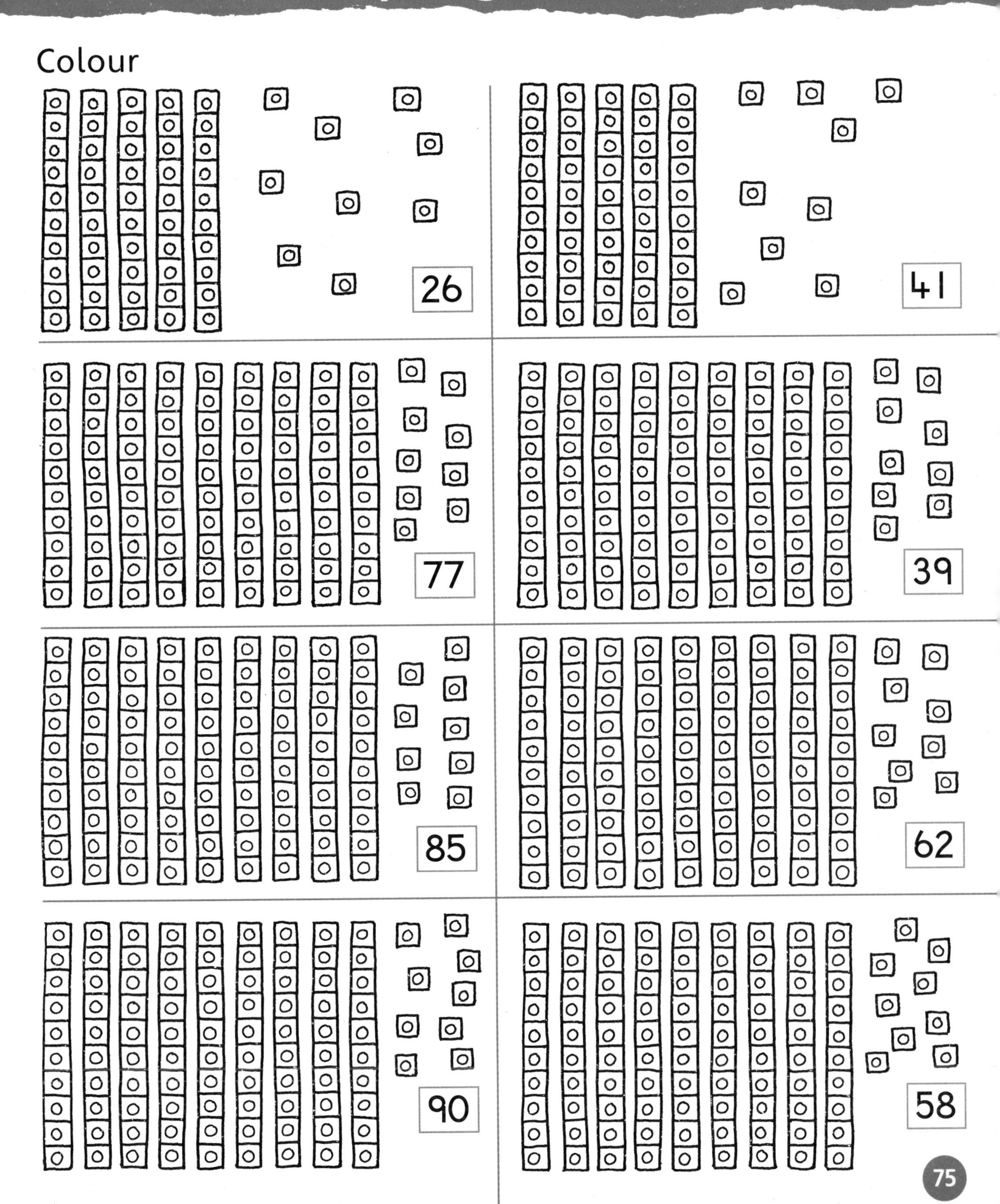

Adding groups of ten

The children already have some stickers.

They buy some more. How many do they have now? Write

10 + 10 =

20 + 20 =

30 + 20 =

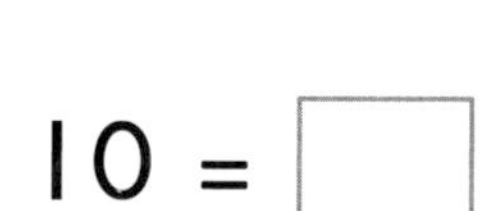

60 + 10 =

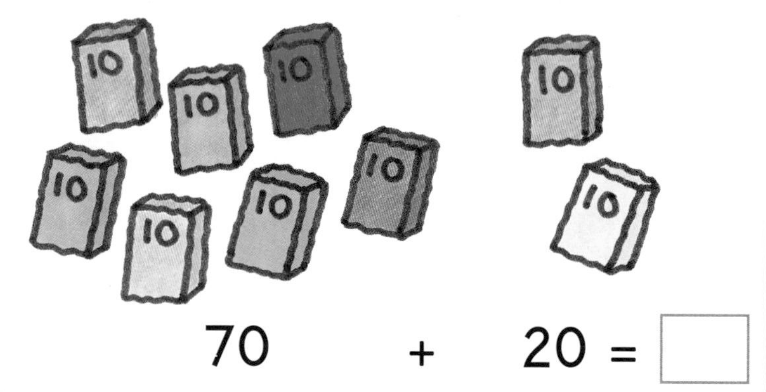

70 + 20 =

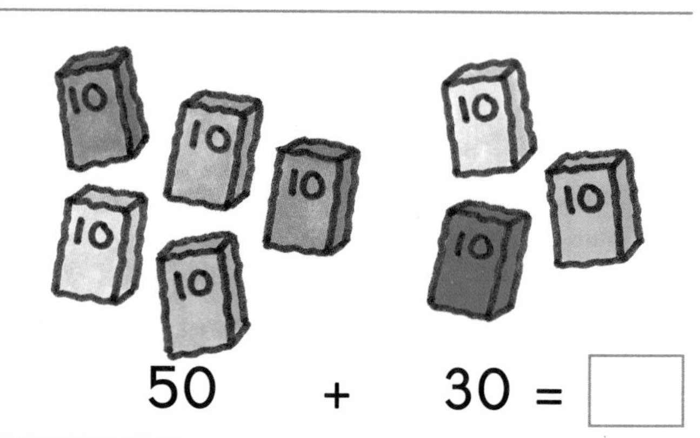

50 + 30 =

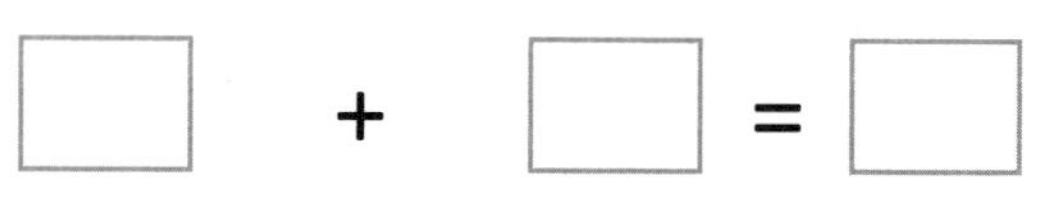

+ =

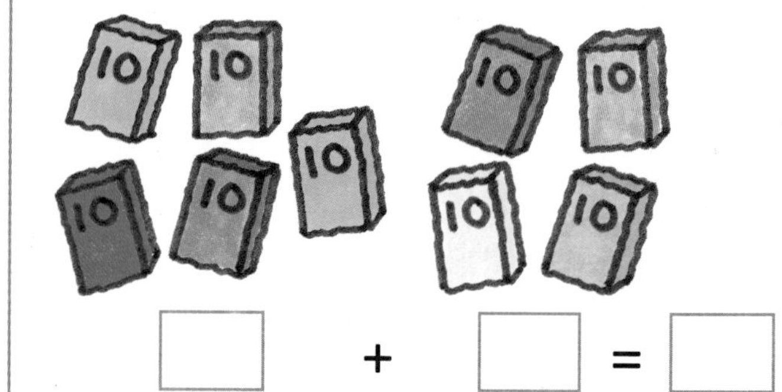

+ =

Dress the clown

Dress Rolo. Use cubes to find out how many ways he can wear these clothes.

Magic cubes

Jess is looking for the magic cube. The magic cube is the one with the largest number. Help her to find it.

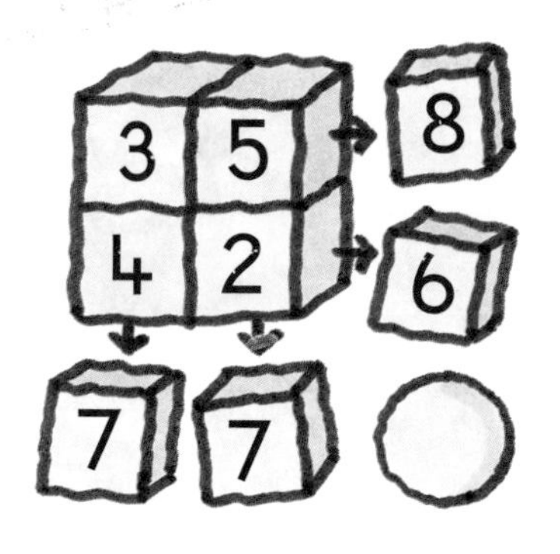

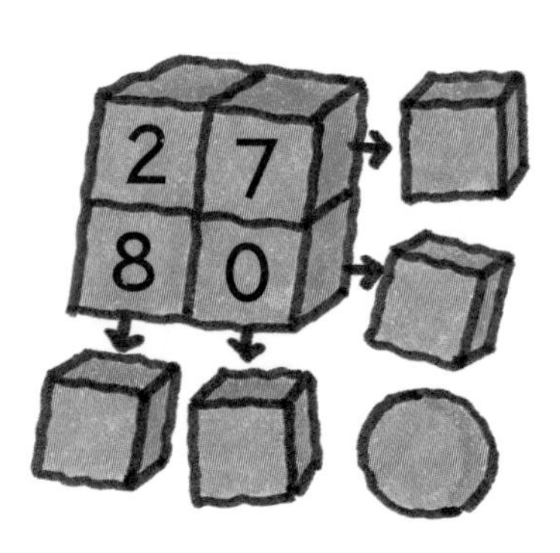

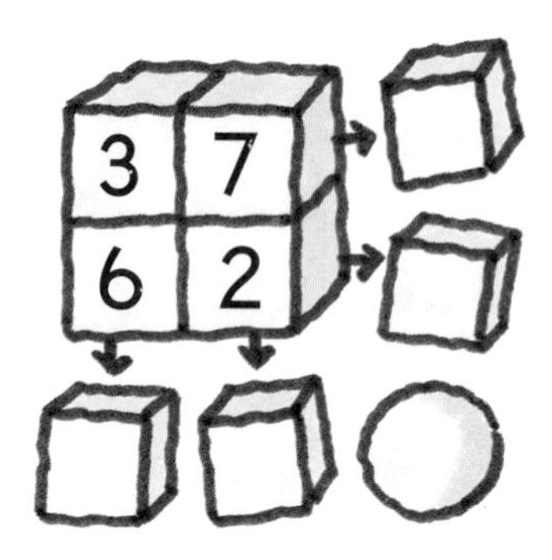

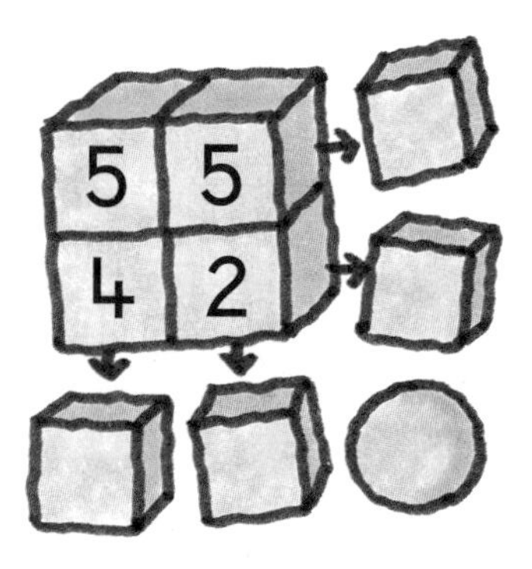

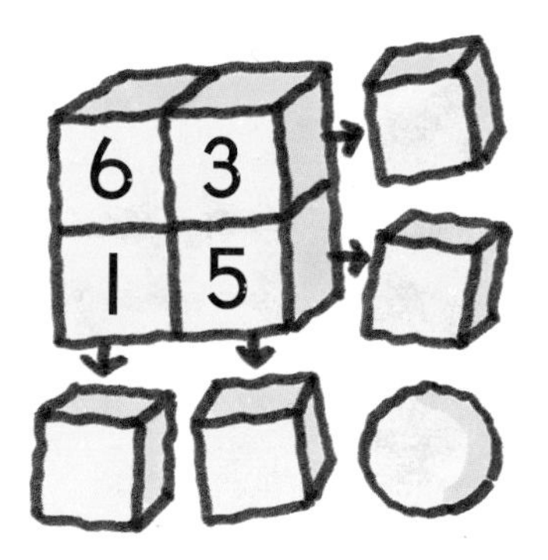

Ordinal numbers

Colour to match.

Think
Talk
Pound City
35c
20c
8c
30c
12c
45c
15c
38c
26c
17c
49c
35c
per 1 kg

How much?

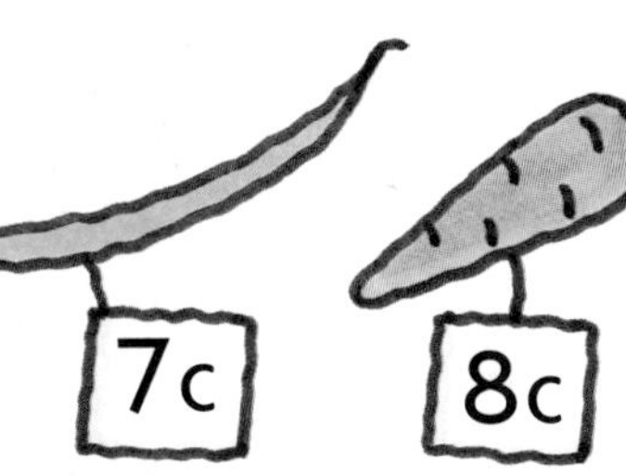

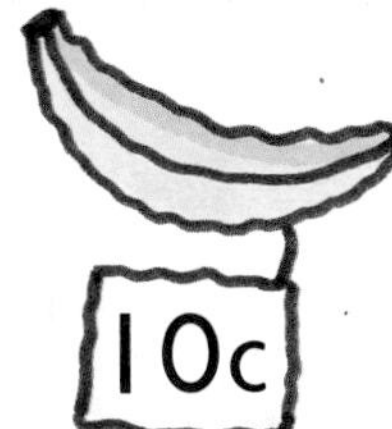

☐ + ☐ = ☐

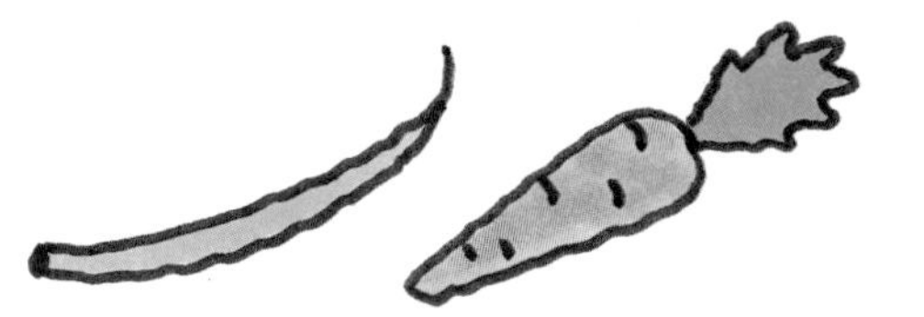

☐ + ☐ = ☐

☐ + ☐ = ☐

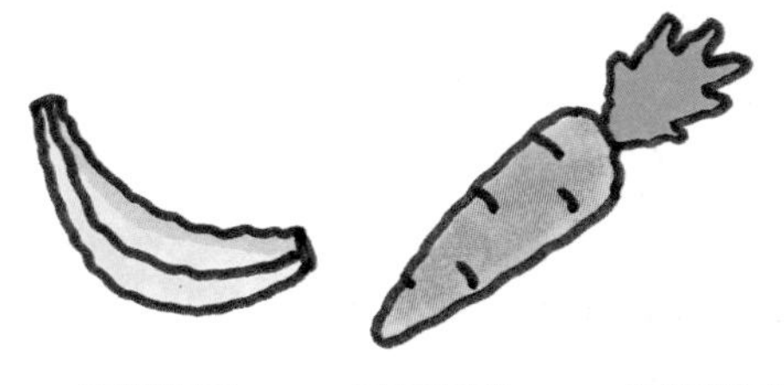

☐ + ☐ = ☐

☐ + ☐ = ☐

☐ + ☐ = ☐

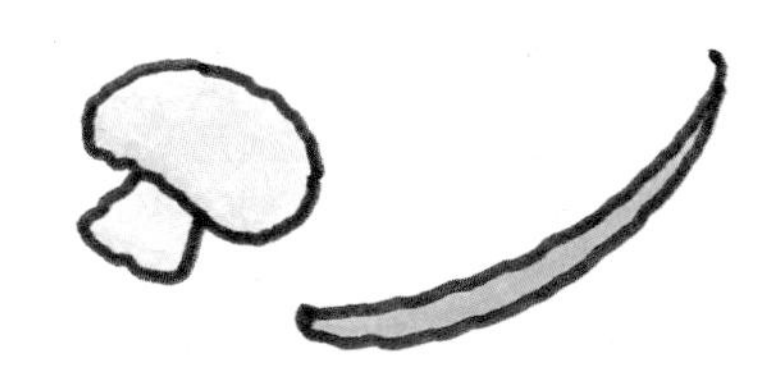

☐ + ☐ = ☐

☐ + ☐ + ☐ = ☐

Number stories: money

Write

I have 7c.

I need ☐ c.

7c + ☐ c = 9c

I have 9c.

I need ☐ c.

9c + ☐ c = 11c

I have 6c.

I need ☐ c.

6c + ☐ c = 12c

I have 8c.

I need ☐ c.

8c + ☐ c = 16c

I have 9c.

I need ☐ c.

9c + ☐ c = 10c

I have 6c.

I need ☐ c.

6c + ☐ c = 10c

I have 7c.

I need ☐ c.

7c + ☐ c = 14c

I have 9c.

I need ☐ c.

9c + ☐ c = 12c

Counting back

Use the numberline. Subtract

1	2	3	4	5	6	7	8	9	10	11	12	13	14	15	16	17	18	19	20

9 – 2 = ☐ 16 – 7 = ☐ 15 – 7 = ☐

12 – 3 = ☐ 10 – 3 = ☐ 19 – 9 = ☐

13 – 4 = ☐ 14 – 5 = ☐ 9 – 6 = ☐

12 – 5 = ☐ 18 – 9 = ☐ 17 – 10 = ☐

16 – 8 = ☐ 13 – 6 = ☐ 14 – 8 = ☐

15 – 6 = ☐ 11 – 2 = ☐ 16 – 9 = ☐

15 – 8 = ☐ 14 – 7 = ☐ 19 – 10 = ☐

Counting on and counting back

Count on and count back.

1	2	3	4	5	6	7	8	9	10	11

3 + 3 = ☐

1	2	3	4	5	6	7	8	9	10	11

6 – 3 = ☐

1	2	3	4	5	6	7	8	9	10	11

6 + 5 = ☐

1	2	3	4	5	6	7	8	9	10	11

11 – 5 = ☐

Now try these. Use your number strip.

5 + 5 = ☐ 4 + 4 = ☐ 6 + 6 = ☐ 4 + 3 = ☐
10 – 5 = ☐ 8 – 4 = ☐ 12 – 6 = ☐ 7 – 3 = ☐

5 + 6 = ☐ 7 + 6 = ☐ 8 + 9 = ☐ 10 + 9 = ☐
11 – 6 = ☐ 13 – 6 = ☐ 17 – 9 = ☐ 19 – 9 = ☐

Half $\frac{1}{2}$

Colour and write.

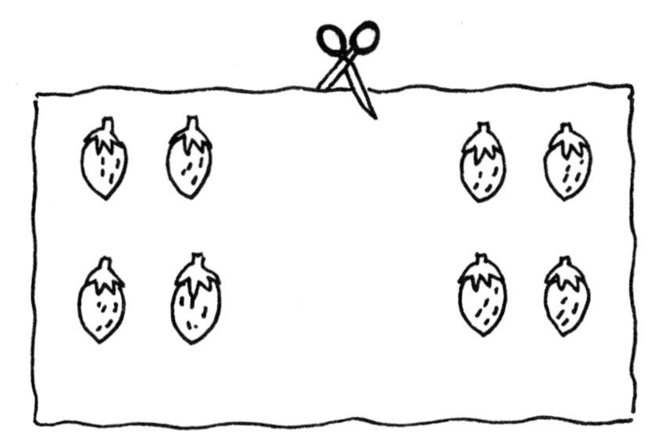

half of 8 is ☐

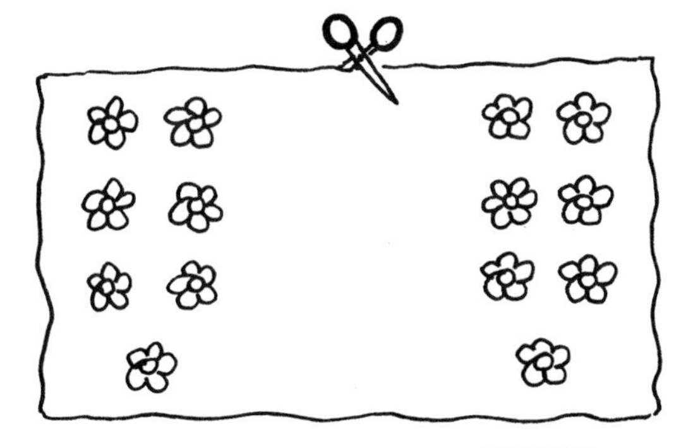

half of 14 is ☐

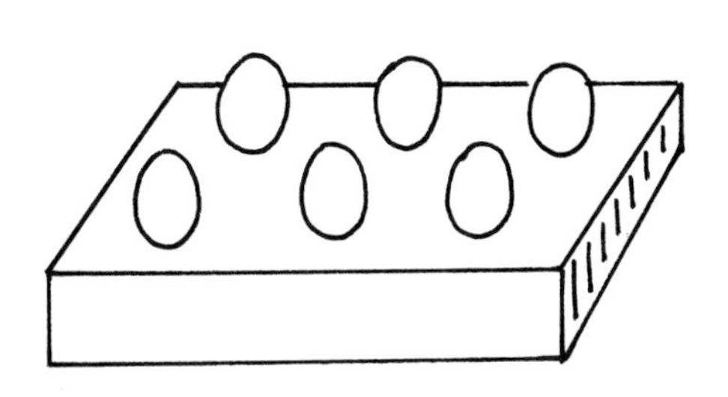

half of 6 is ☐

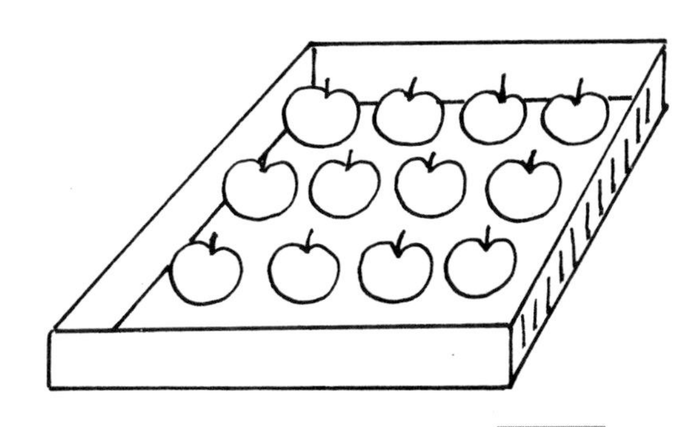

half of 12 is ☐

half of ☐ is ☐

$\frac{1}{2}$ of ☐ is ☐

Use cubes to find these.

$\frac{1}{2}$ of 10 = ☐

$\frac{1}{2}$ of 16 = ☐

$\frac{1}{2}$ of 18 = ☐

$\frac{1}{2}$ of 20 = ☐

Data

Write

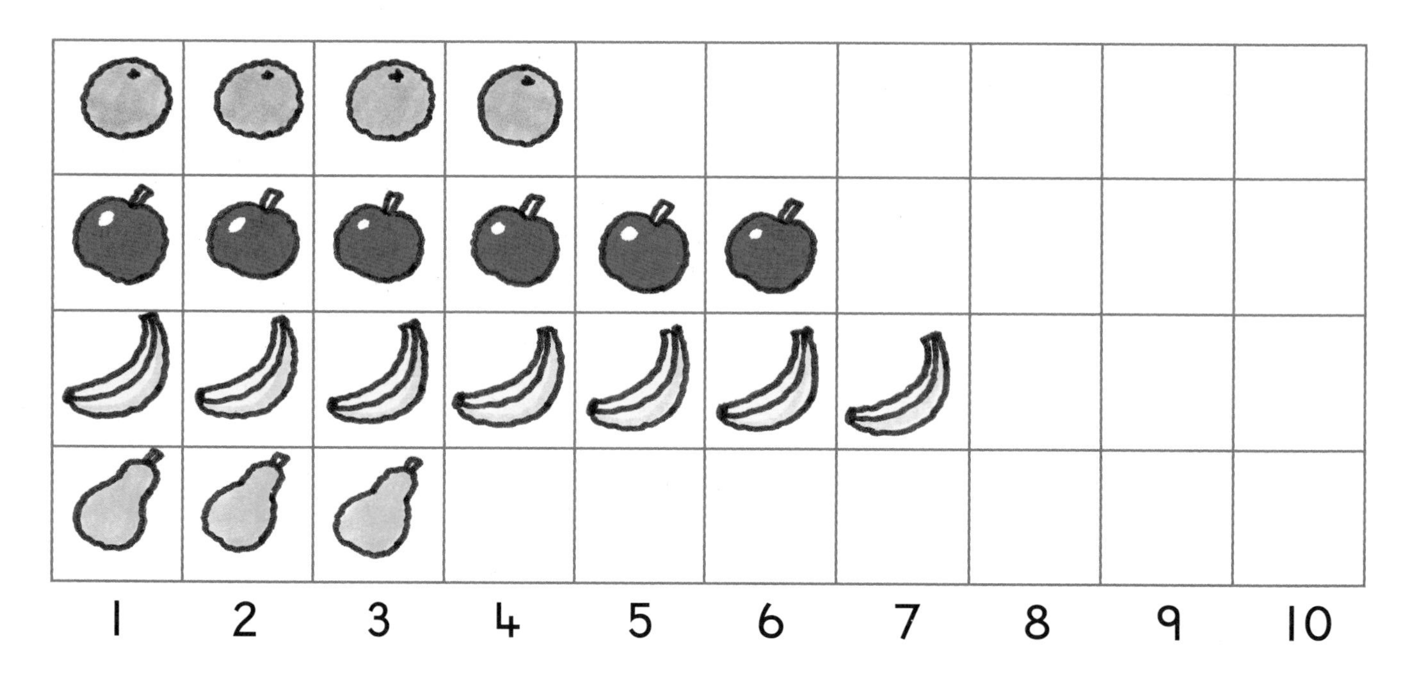

How many?

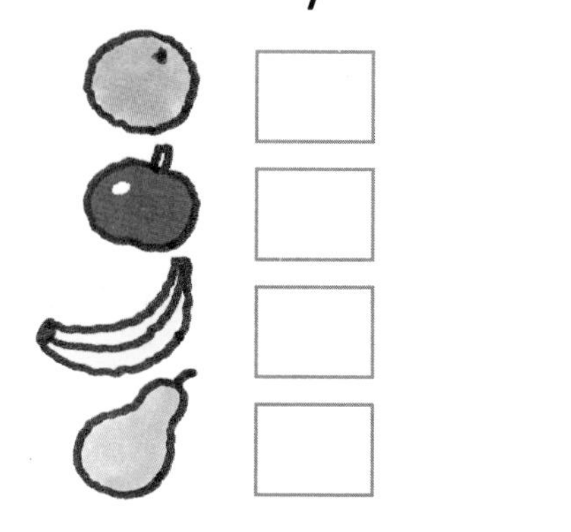

How many more bananas than oranges?

How many less pears than apples?

Make a pictogram of the favourite fruits in your class.

Subtraction –

How many are left?

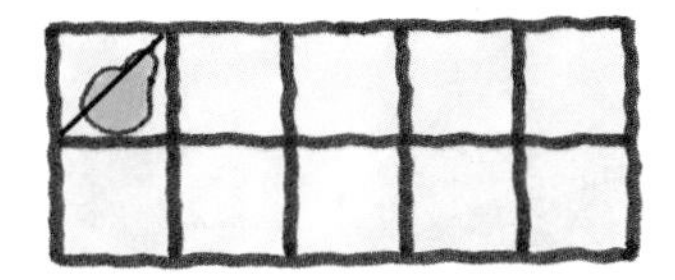

Mary had 11 pears.

She sold 3.

There are ☐ pears left.

11 – 3 = ☐

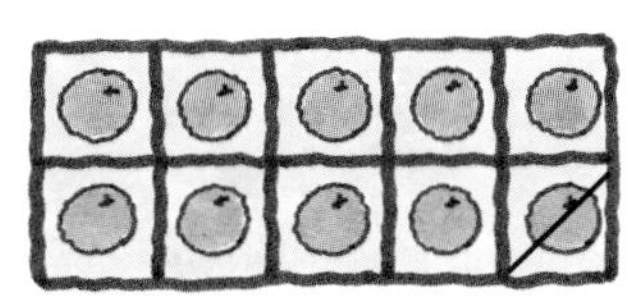
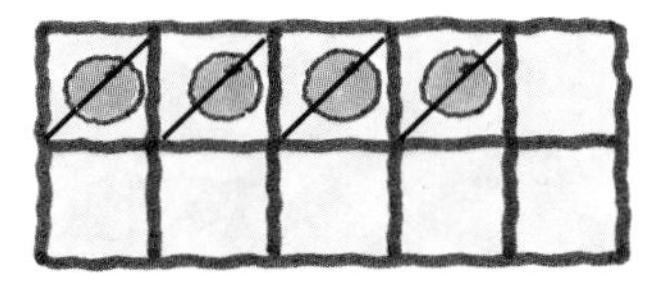

Mary had 14 oranges.

She sold 5.

There are ☐ oranges left.

14 – 5 = ☐

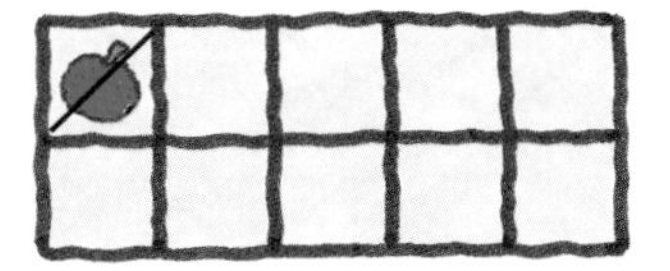

Mary had 11 apples.

She sold 4.

There are ☐ apples left.

11 – 4 = ☐

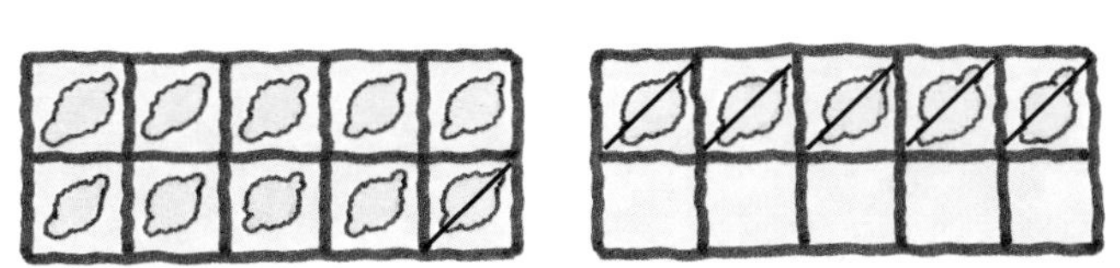

Mary had 15 lemons.

She sold 6.

There are ☐ lemons left.

15 – 6 = ☐

Now try these. Use counters and ten frames.

12 – 3 = ☐	12 – 5 = ☐	14 – 6 = ☐
13 – 5 = ☐	13 – 4 = ☐	11 – 2 = ☐
14 – 4 = ☐	12 – 4 = ☐	16 – 7 = ☐

Money

Colour the coins.

Money

What coins would you use to buy the fruit? Draw

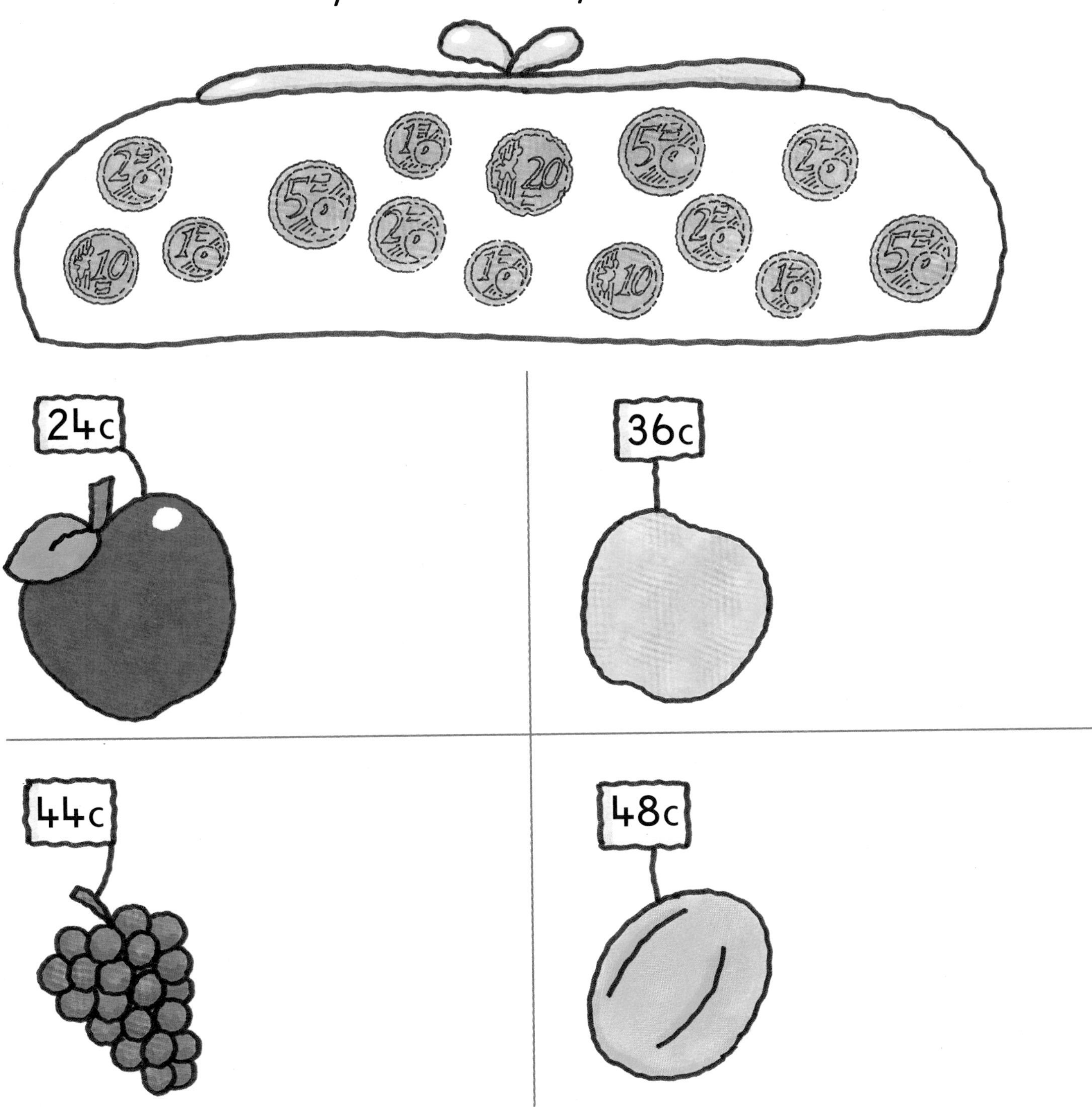

Can you buy the fruit using other coins? Draw

Money

Write

 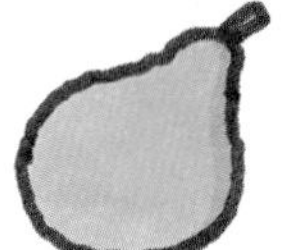

had bought

20c – 15c = ☐ c

had bought

20c – 17c = ☐ c

had bought

20c – ☐ c = ☐ c

had bought

20c – ☐ c = ☐ c

 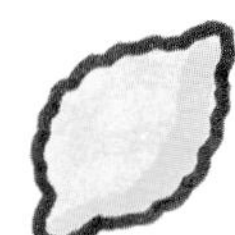

had bought

had bought

had bought

had bought

☐ c – ☐ c = ☐ c

Number stories

Write

$\square + \square = \square$

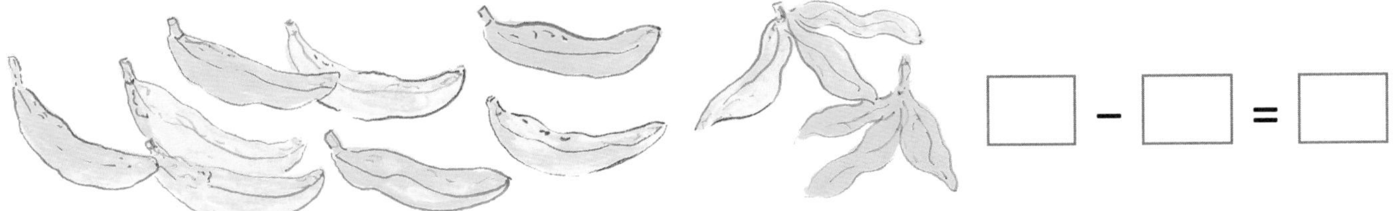

$\square - \square = \square$

Tom had 6 apples. He bought 4 more apples.
How many has he now? Draw and write.

Niamh had 12 oranges. She gave 4 of them to Kim's Dad.
How many has she now?

Draw and write.

$8 + 8 = \square$

$13 - 9 = \square$

100 square

Fill in the missing numbers and colour.

1	2	3	4	5	6	7	8	9	10
11				15	16	17	18	19	20
21	22		24	25	26	27		29	30
					36				40
41	42		44	45	46	47		49	50
51	52		54	55	56	57	58	59	60
61				65	66		68	69	70
71		73		75			78	79	
81		83		85	86				90
91		93		95	96		98		100

Missing numbers

Write the number after.

Write the number before.

Write the number between.

Fill in the missing numbers.

21 22 23 ☐ ☐ ☐ ☐ ☐ ☐ 30

31 32 ☐ ☐ ☐ 36 ☐ ☐ ☐ ☐

41 ☐ 43 ☐ ☐ ☐ ☐ ☐ 49 50

☐ 52 ☐ 54 ☐ ☐ ☐ ☐ ☐ 60

1 to 100

Join the dots.

Weight

Niamh needs your help to sort these things.
Ring and match.

Weight

Write

The ______________ is heavier than the ______________.

The ______________ is lighter than the ______________.

The ______________ weighs the same as the ______________.

Draw

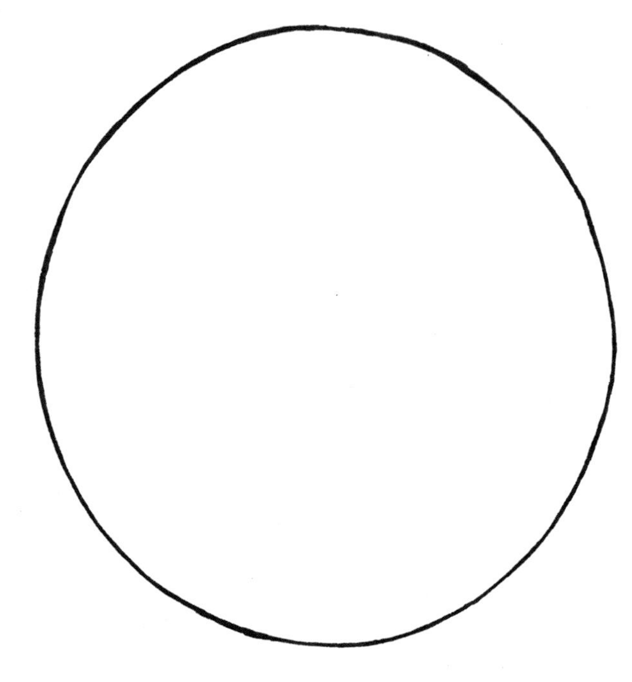

five things
lighter than a pencil

five things
heavier than this book

Weight

Guess and weigh.

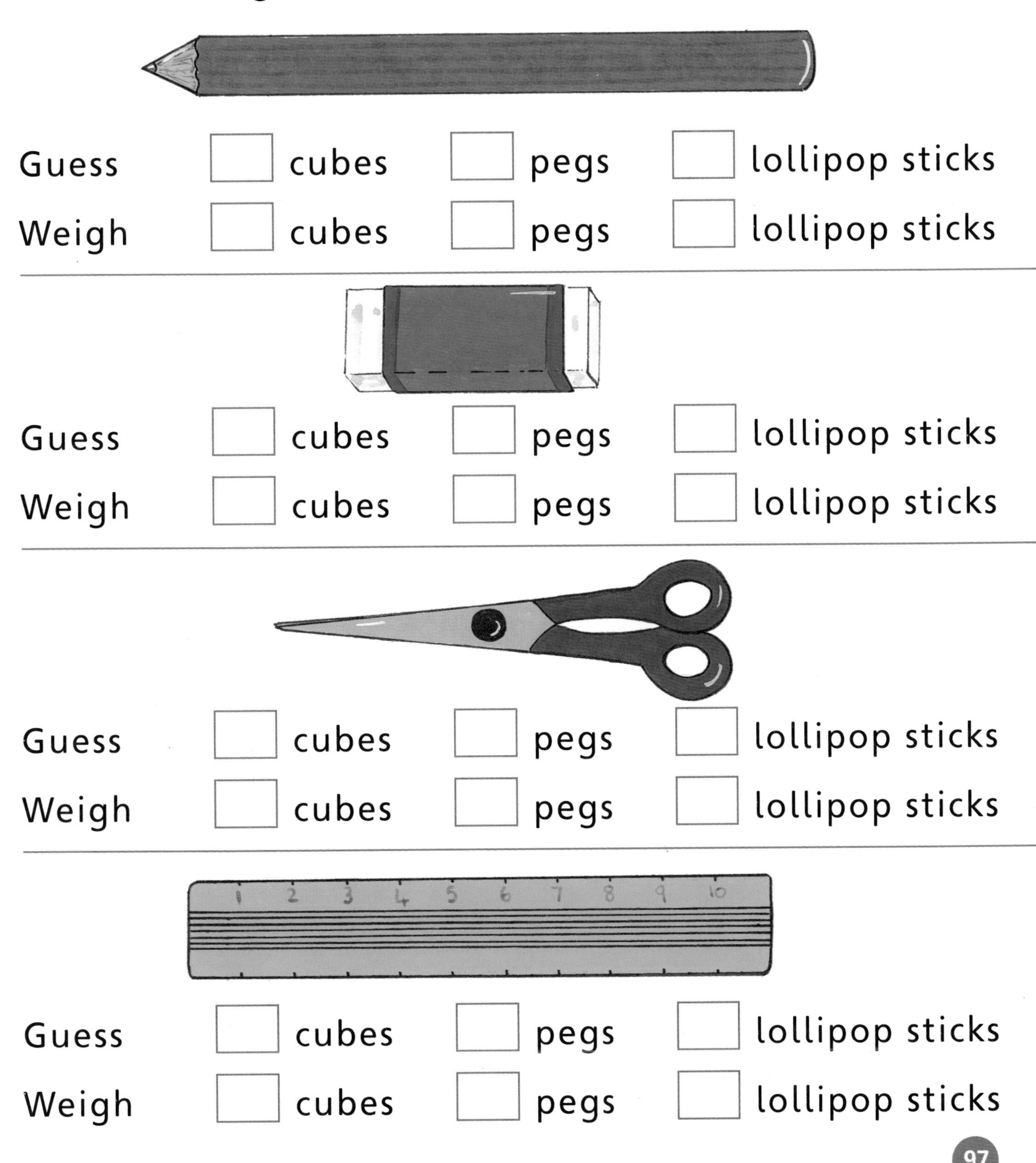

Guess ☐ cubes ☐ pegs ☐ lollipop sticks

Weigh ☐ cubes ☐ pegs ☐ lollipop sticks

Guess ☐ cubes ☐ pegs ☐ lollipop sticks

Weigh ☐ cubes ☐ pegs ☐ lollipop sticks

Guess ☐ cubes ☐ pegs ☐ lollipop sticks

Weigh ☐ cubes ☐ pegs ☐ lollipop sticks

Guess ☐ cubes ☐ pegs ☐ lollipop sticks

Weigh ☐ cubes ☐ pegs ☐ lollipop sticks

The kilogram

Find and draw things in your classroom that weigh about a kilogram.

Find and draw things that are more than a kilogram.
Find and draw things that are less than a kilogram.

Nearest ten

Match each butterfly to the daisy that has the nearest number ten.

Number patterns

Fill in the number patterns. Write the last number on each ladder in the box of apples.

Ring the tree where Liam got the most apples.

Addition

Kate is putting eggs in boxes. Help her to count.

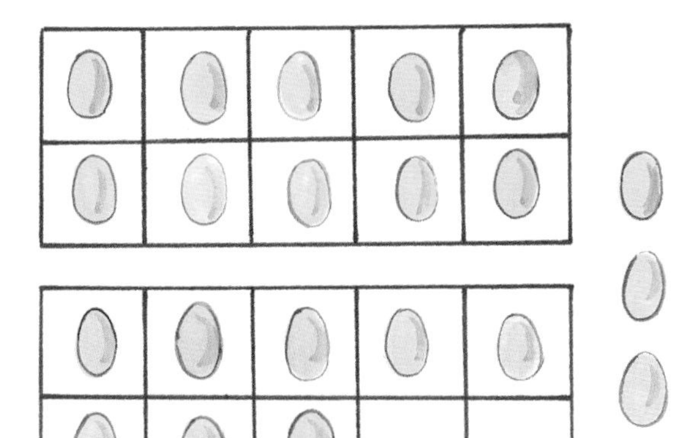

18 + 3 = ☐

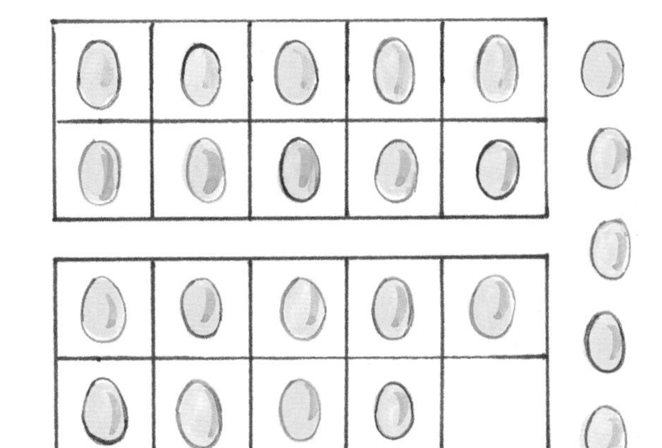

19 + 5 = ☐

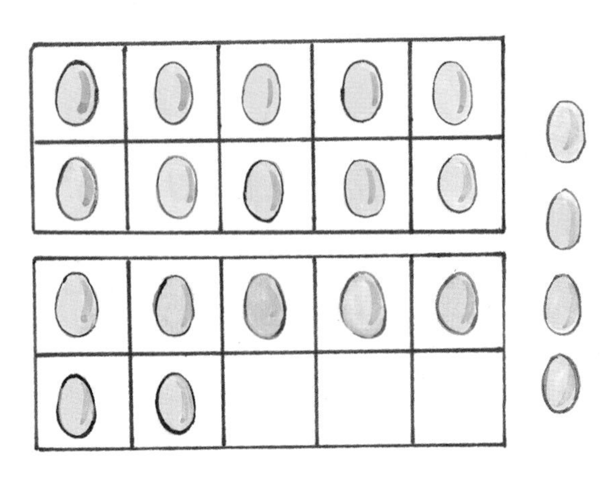

17 + 4 = ☐

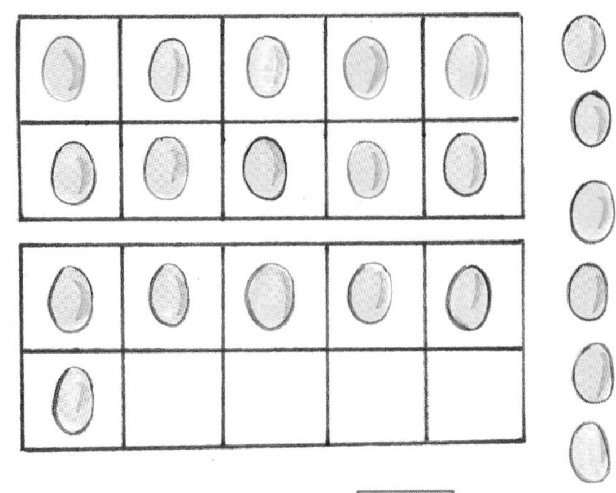

16 + 6 = ☐

Now try these. Use counters and ten frames.

18 + 6 = ☐	16 + 7 = ☐	19 + 9 = ☐	14 + 8 = ☐
18 + 9 = ☐	17 + 5 = ☐	11 + 9 = ☐	16 + 5 = ☐
19 + 7 = ☐	13 + 8 = ☐	15 + 6 = ☐	17 + 7 = ☐

Adding tens

Add and write.

Now try these.

37	+10 → ☐	+10 → ☐	+20 → ☐	+20 → ☐
24	+10 → ☐	+10 → ☐	+20 → ☐	+20 → ☐
19	+10 → ☐	+10 → ☐	+20 → ☐	+20 → ☐

Addition

Add and write.

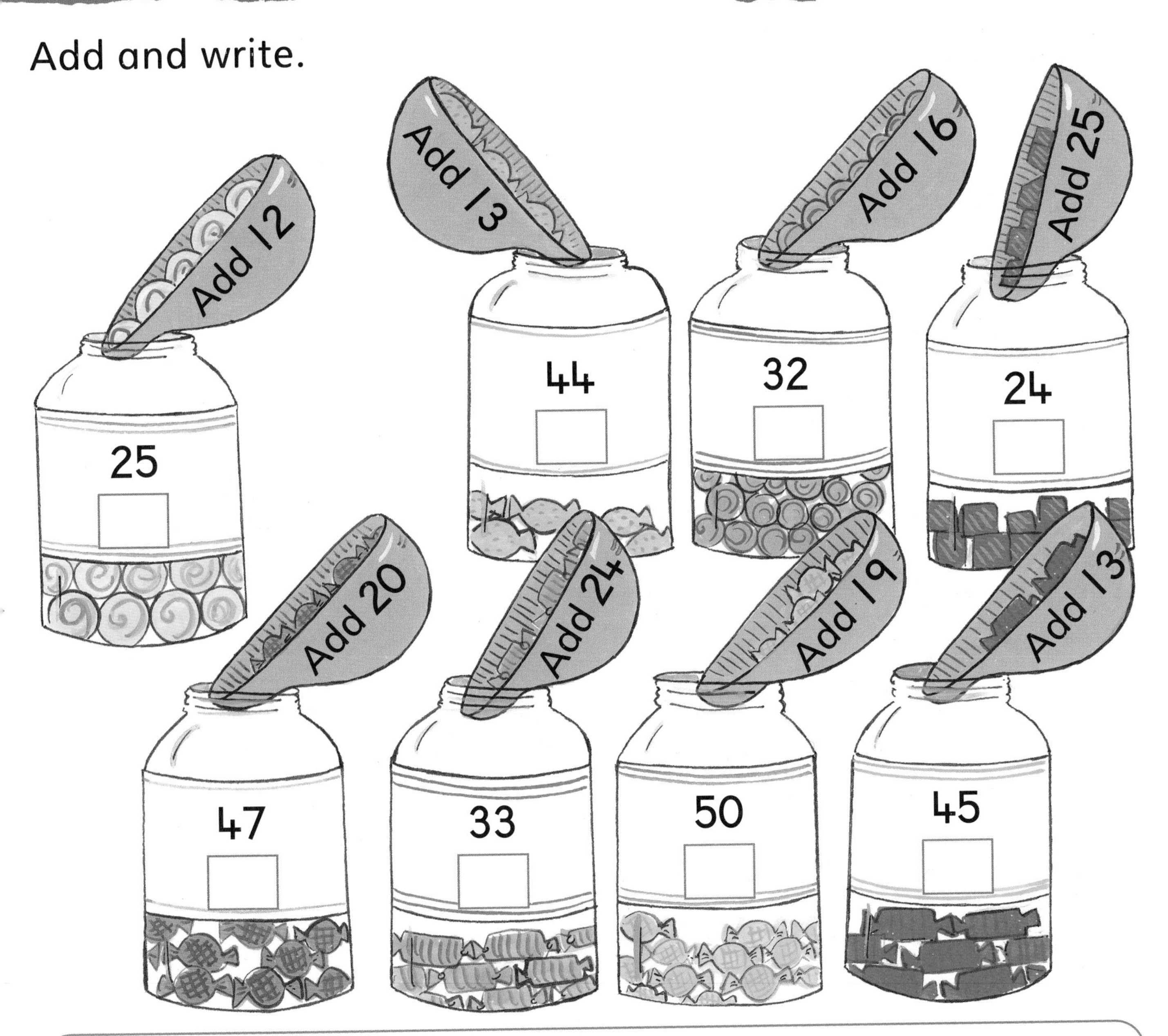

Now try these.

28 + 11 = ☐ 34 + 14 = ☐ 42 + 17 = ☐

60 + 12 = ☐ 24 + 23 = ☐ 36 + 21 = ☐

43 + 25 = ☐ 31 + 33 = ☐ 24 + 24 = ☐

Think
Talk

Time

Write

Time

What time is it? Put the pictures in the right order.

$\frac{1}{2}$ past

1

Time

Show the times.

2 o'clock

$\frac{1}{2}$ past 3

12 o'clock

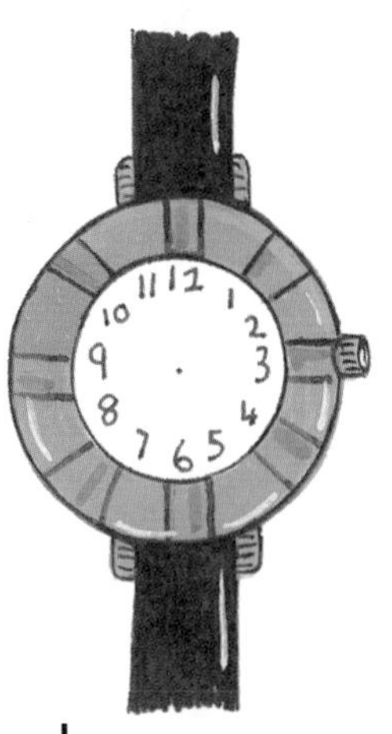

$\frac{1}{2}$ past 10

$\frac{1}{2}$ past 8

6 o'clock

$\frac{1}{2}$ past 12

9 o'clock

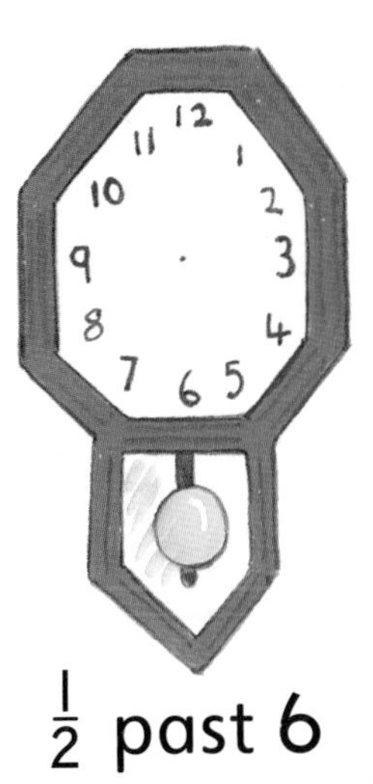

$\frac{1}{2}$ past 6

Group counting

How many?

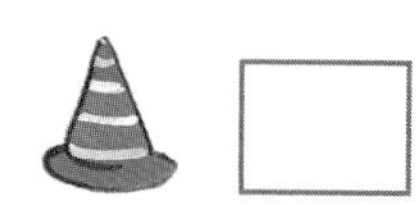

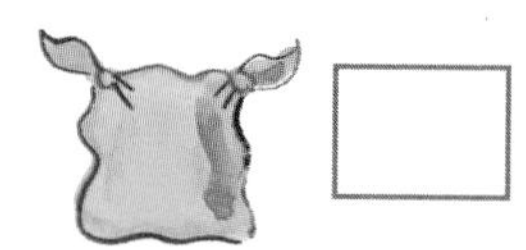

Write the missing numbers.

Addition

Add and colour to match the ribbons.

18 + 5	28 + 4	39 + 5	48 + 5	58 + 4
39 + 2	45 + 8	19 + 6	57 + 6	28 + 9
47 + 7	13 + 8	55 + 8	27 + 6	38 + 7
56 + 7	37 + 4	29 + 3	17 + 9	46 + 8
25 + 6	58 + 8	49 + 2	36 + 6	15 + 7

21 22 23 24 25 26 27 28 29 30

31 32 33 34 35 36 37 38 39 40

41 42 43 44 45 46 47 48 49 50

51 52 53 54 55 56 57 58 59 60

61 62 63 64 65 66 67 68 69 70

Estimation

Guess

18 + 29

Guess ☐

23 + 31

Guess ☐

37 + 19

Guess ☐

43 + 27

Guess ☐

38 + 34

Guess ☐

49 – 18

Guess ☐

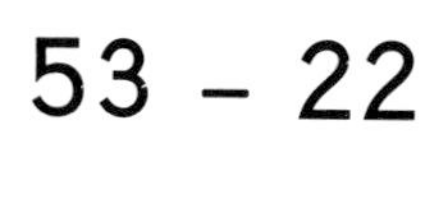

53 – 22

Guess ☐

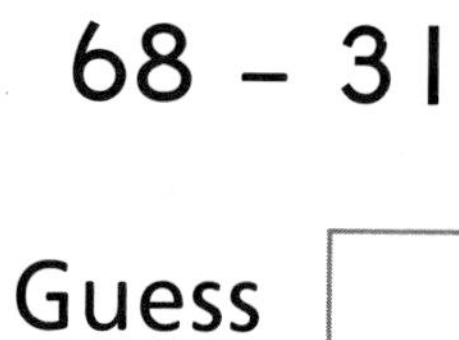

68 – 31

Guess ☐

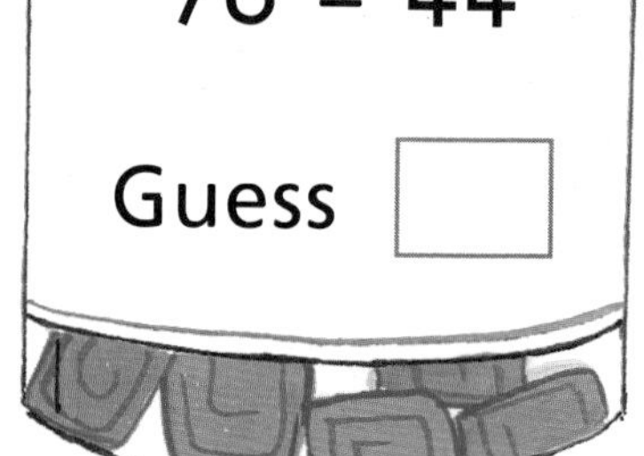

76 – 44

Guess ☐

Calendar

Colour the months to match the seasons.

Spring

Summer

Autumn

Winter

January

February

March

April

May

June

July

August

September

October

November

December

Time

Show the times and write.

Sports Day

10 o'clock: three-legged race

$\frac{1}{2}$ past 10: sack race

11 o'clock: snacks

$\frac{1}{2}$ past 11: obstacle race

12 o'clock: egg and spoon race

$\frac{1}{2}$ past 12: lunch

1 o'clock: relay race

$\frac{1}{2}$ past 1: tug of war

2 o'clock: home

What happens $\frac{1}{2}$ hour after the three-legged race?

____

What happens $\frac{1}{2}$ hour after the egg and spoon race?

____

What happens $\frac{1}{2}$ hour after the tug of war?

____

Calendar

On what days do their birthdays fall? Write

March

Monday	Tuesday	Wednesday	Thursday	Friday	Saturday	Sunday
		1	2	3	4	5
6	7	8	9	10	11	12
13	14	15	16	17	18	19
20	21	22	23	24	25	26
27	28	29	30	31		

6th March

18th March

1st March

12th March

21st March

31st March

On what day does your birthday fall this year? ____________

On what day does Christmas fall this year? ____________

How many are left?

Now try these.

27 – 13 = ☐ 34 – 12 = ☐ 56 – 14 = ☐

48 – 25 = ☐ 49 – 33 = ☐ 67 – 41 = ☐

69 – 19 = ☐ 77 – 22 = ☐ 83 – 52 = ☐

Capacity

Who gets the most? ___________________________

Who gets the least? ___________________________

Who gets about the same? ______________________

Draw things that hold drinks.

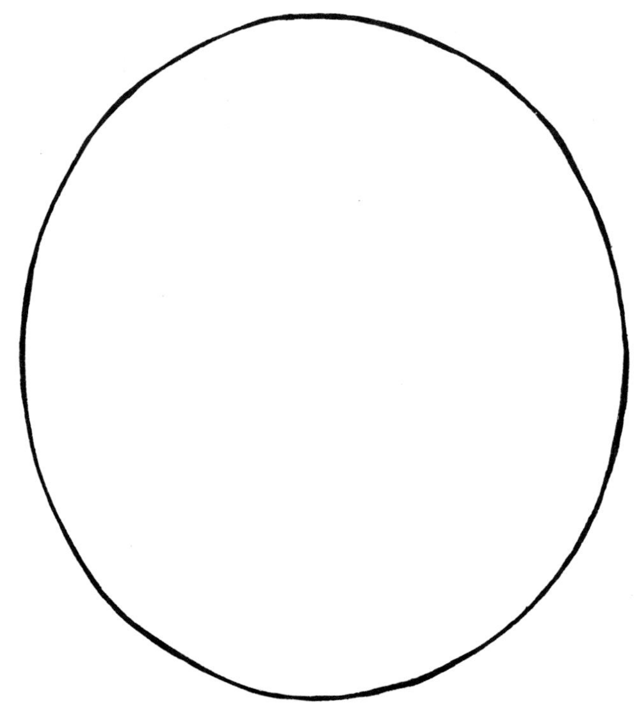

Capacity

Guess and measure.

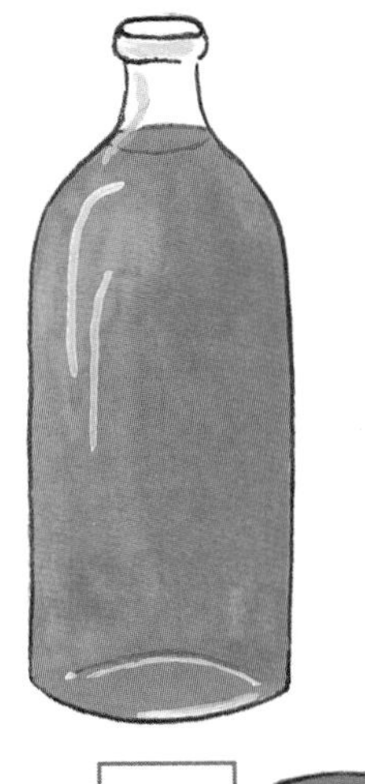

Guess

Count

Guess 

Count 

Guess 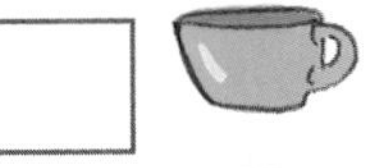

Count

Guess  

Count 

What holds the most? Draw
What holds the least? Draw

Capacity

Guess and measure. Use a spoon or beaker.

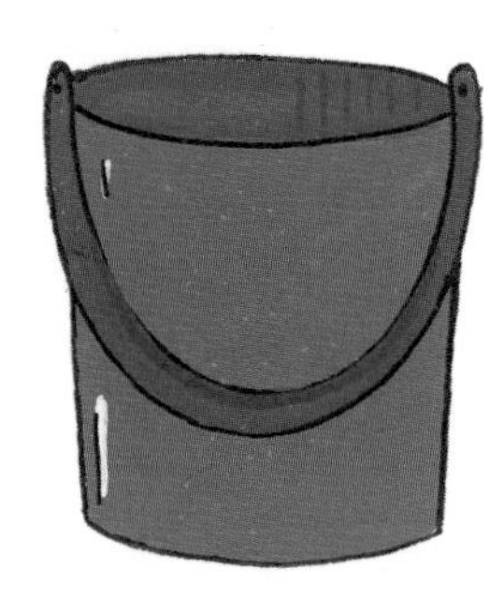

Guess

Count

Guess

Count

Guess

Count

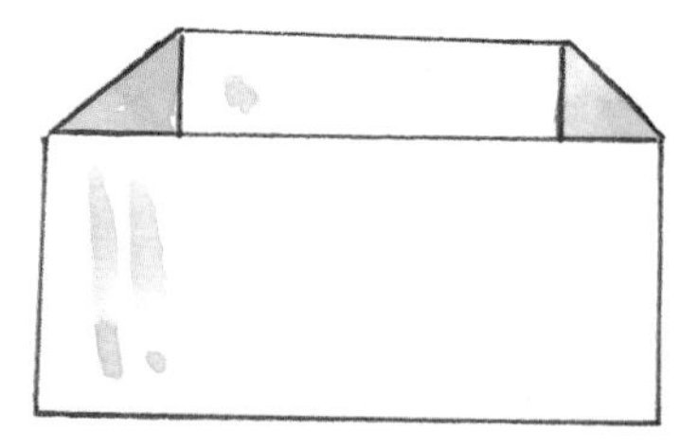

Guess

Count

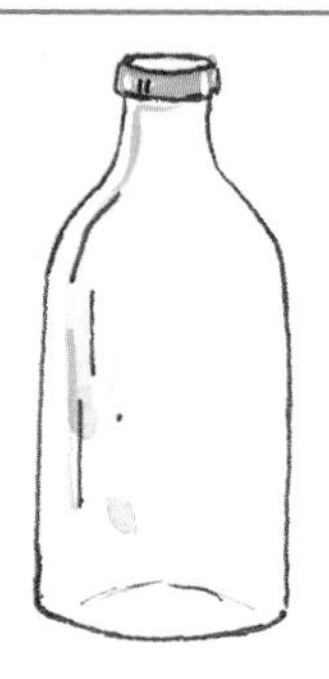

Guess 

Count 

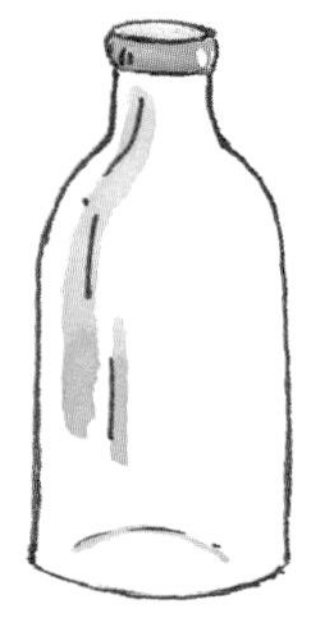

Guess 

Count 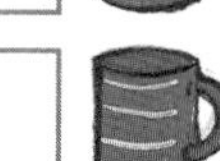

The litre

Find and draw things that hold about a litre.

Find and draw things that hold more than a litre.
Find and draw things that hold less than a litre.

Number patterns

Fill in the number patterns.

Write the last number on each ladder in the box of apples.

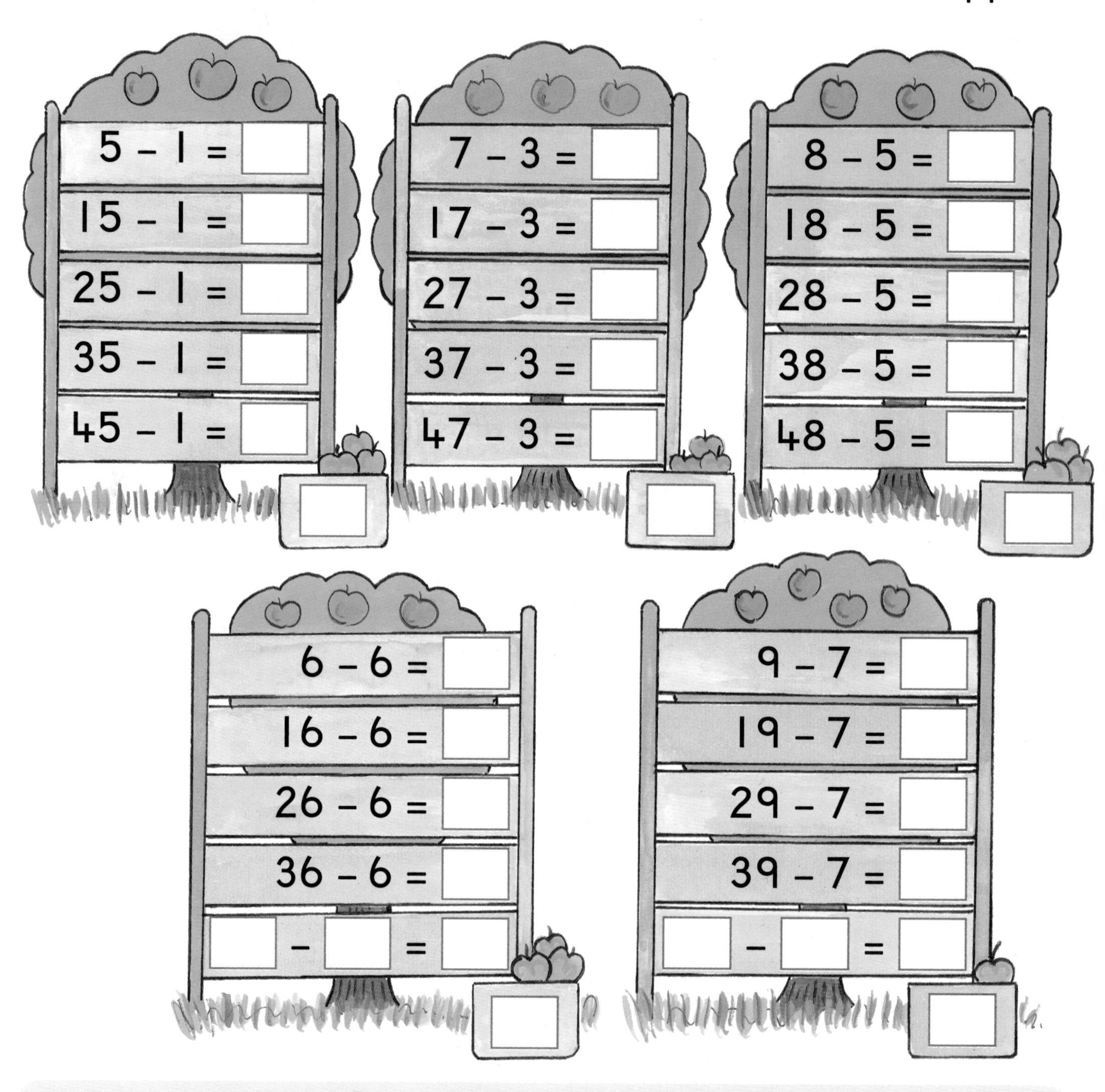

Ring the tree where Kate got the least apples.

Subtraction –

How many are left?

Now try these.

34 – 20 = ☐ 72 – 30 = ☐ 88 – 40 = ☐

35 – 30 = ☐ 54 – 30 = ☐ 94 – 40 = ☐

48 – 30 = ☐ 65 – 30 = ☐ 79 – 40 = ☐

Capacity

Ring and colour the glasses.

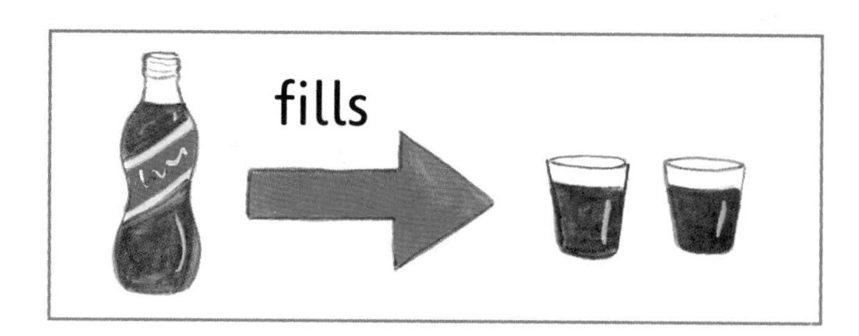

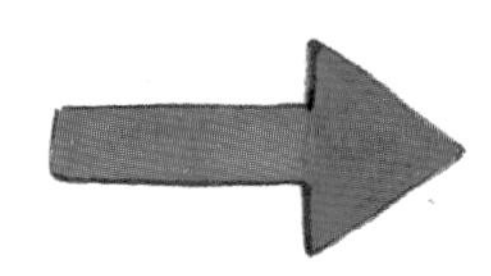

Ring and colour the bottles.

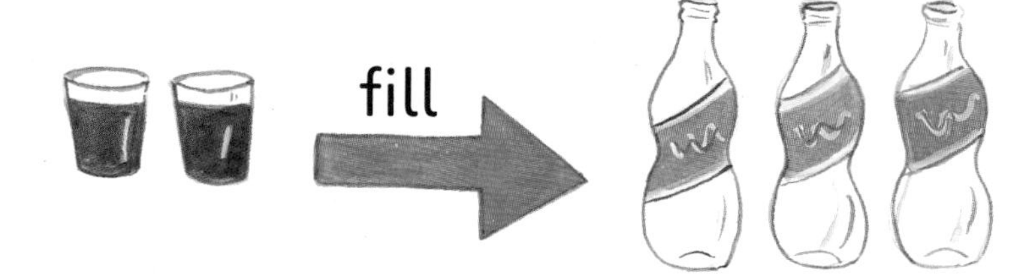

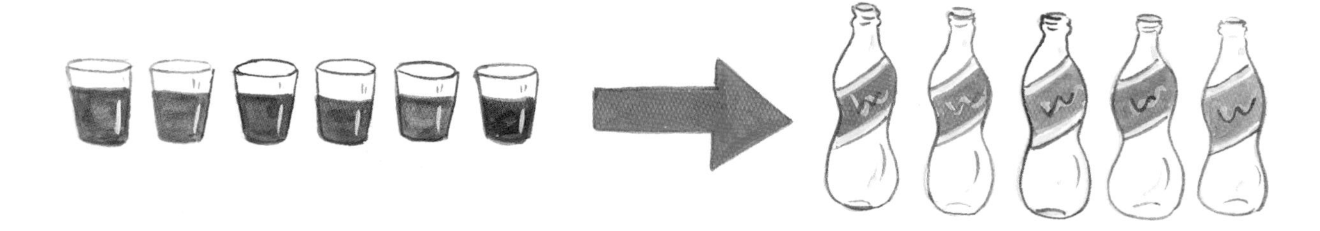

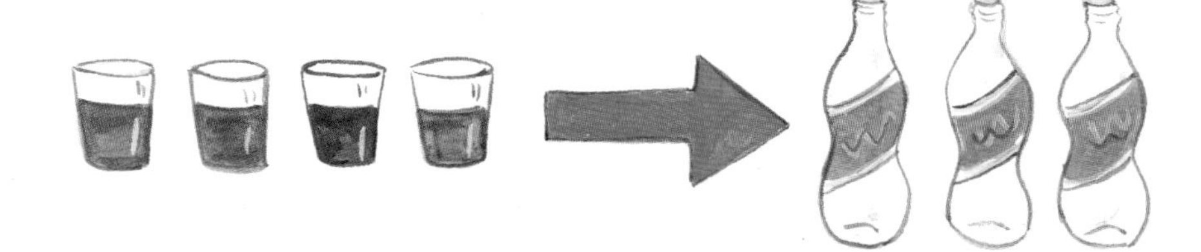

Data

Sort

	I like	I don't like
drink		
not a drink		

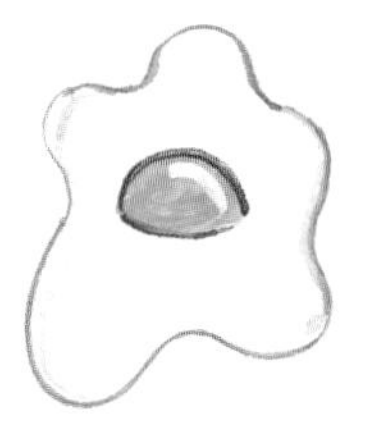

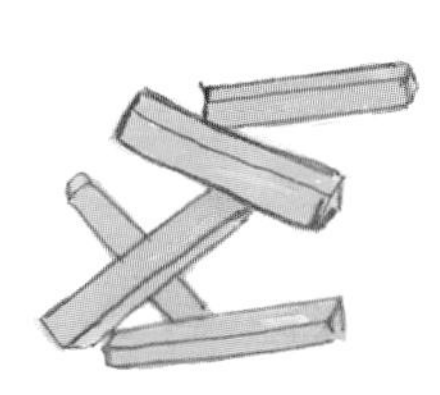

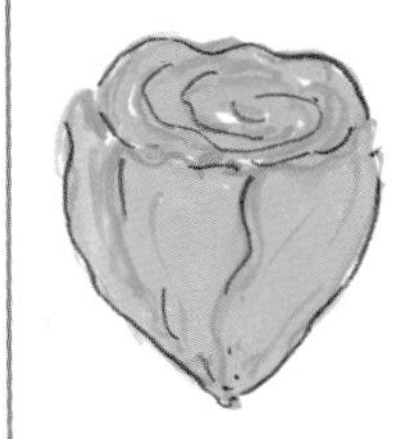

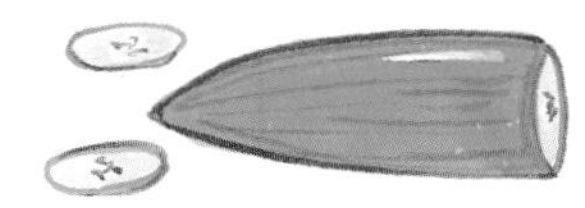

Data

These are the drinks of the First Class children on Sports Day. How many?

Make a pictogram.

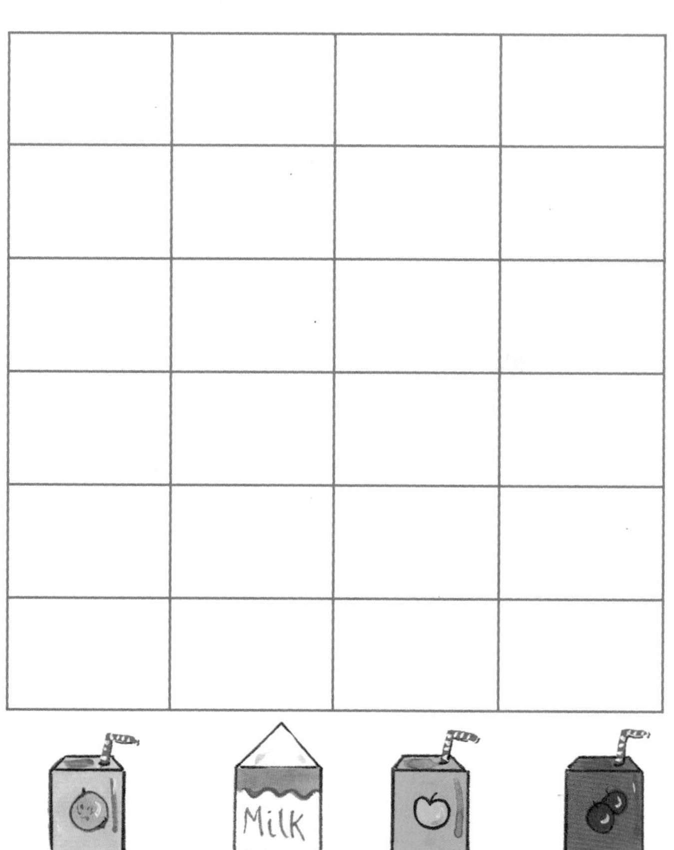

Addition

Help the children to find the path to the beach.

Add and colour.

25	72	81	93	67	32	87	68	95	39
31	64	37	70	24	96	26	4	55	14
42	3	65	54	60	41	52	77	63	51
53	85	40	11	49	6	38	13	73	89
94	28	79	23	15	43	16	33	19	27
61	66	91	62	22	75	56	1	80	9
10	50	82	69	90	34	20	59	97	88
29	12	71	47	86	7	92	35	18	27
8	84	48	44	21	30	98	46	66	76
36	17	74	57	33	45	83	58	78	99

$19 + 6 =$ ☐

$50 + 30 =$ ☐

$96 - 20 =$ ☐

$49 + 15 =$ ☐

$98 - 10 =$ ☐

$47 + 19 =$ ☐

$35 + 14 =$ ☐

$60 + 10 =$ ☐

$15 + 8 =$ ☐

$62 - 41 =$ ☐

$95 - 35 =$ ☐

$89 + 10 =$ ☐

$99 - 20 =$ ☐

$24 + 26 =$ ☐

$60 - 30 =$ ☐

$28 + 19 =$ ☐

$77 - 40 =$ ☐

$36 + 23 =$ ☐

$79 - 52 =$ ☐

$23 + 69 =$ ☐

$94 - 23 =$ ☐

Looking back

Talk and write.